Delicious&Nutritious

Healthy home cooking for older people

Adapting and freezing dishes for home cooking

Most of the recipes in the book can be adapted for one or two people. However, if the dish includes a sauce, you might decide to make the full quantity and use it for a dish the next day.

We don't freeze foods in Barchester homes as an extra precaution when serving food to vulnerable adults. However, some foods are ideal to freeze if you are cooking for yourself or your family at home. All of the soups, cakes and pastry dishes freeze well. Avoid freezing foods with raw or lightly cooked vegetables, such as panache or salads, as they do not freeze well due to the high water content. Stews and casseroles also freeze well. As a rule, avoid freezing rice, chicken and fish dishes, if possible, as they tend to be more susceptible to food poisoning – better to be safe than sorry.

First published in Great Britain by
Simon & Schuster UK Ltd. 2007
A CBS Company

Copyright © Barchester Healthcare

Simon & Schuster UK Ltd
Africa House, 64-78 Kingsway,
London WC2B 6AH

1 3 5 7 9 10 8 6 4 2

Design: **Fiona Andreanelli**
Photography: **Tony Briscoe**
Prop styling: **Jo Harris**
Food styling: **Sara Lewis**

Printed and bound in China

ISBN 1 847 370 543

Thanks

My thanks to all the Barchester residents, chefs, home managers and other staff who have sent recipes, offered ideas and have been incredibly supportive in completing this book.

Thank you to both of my wonderful teams – the hospitality team and the learning and development team – as they were always on hand to read something through or offer advice. They were amazingly supportive, as always. Particular thanks to Stephanie Wilkinson for tirelessly typing and retyping the recipes. I am so grateful to Rebecca Haggar, Catering Manager at Castle Care, Irene Lewis, Head Chef at Southview and Brian Lane, Head Chef at Tandridge Heights, for all their support, ideas, recipe tips and advice. Charlotte Oppong-Agyare, the Barchester Marketing Manager, was always on hand to help and support the project.

My family need medals for being so patient and indulging me with yet another of my projects, which always demand so much of my home time. We enjoyed some eclectic Sunday lunches, when I gave my sons Michael and Simon (and whoever happened to be in the house at the time) recipes to test. My long-suffering partner Geoff was frequently asked to help with editing.

Contributors

Sheena Wyllie – the Memory Lane Programme Manager. Sheena was responsible for the Dementia input. Her expertise and her passion help us to ensure that every aspect of the work we do at Barchester is resident-centred.

Rob Burcher – Hospitality Specialist. Rob spent many hours calculating the nutritional values of all the dishes, in addition to keeping up his very busy work schedule supporting the care homes.

Claire Baseley (MA MMedSci RNutr), Company Nutritionist at 3663 First for Foodservice, for providing nutritional assistance and support.

Delicious & Nutritious

Healthy home cooking for older people

Foreword by Paul Rankin

Food is so important to us all both socially and nutritionally, and this book does a great job in promoting healthy and enjoyable food for all. It is the first book of its kind; dedicated to providing help and new ideas to those cooking for older friends and family members as well as those cooking for older people in care homes.

In addition to the great recipes, which can be enjoyed by all, the nutritional content and the chefs' tips will help to ensure that everyone can have a balanced diet. The book demonstrates how many old, tried-and-tested recipes can be updated to suit individual needs and modern tastes, and how we can substitute healthier ingredients to provide the best nutritional value.

I have worked with Barchester Healthcare, the national care home provider, for two years now. I have been involved with helping to develop the skills of their chefs, as well as spearheading their 'Cooking with care initiative' to raise the standards of food within care homes. I am so pleased that they have developed this great book, which I hope will inspire all those who read and use it.

There has been much adverse publicity about food in care homes in recent years, and this book offers the sector a great opportunity to get it right.

Contents

Introduction

Nutritional benefits for all

We hope that this recipe book will help to provide balanced meals for older people, whether they are looking after themselves, being cared for as residents or in the community. In addition to this, Barchester Healthcare want to help eliminate poor nutrition, or malnutrition by raising the profile of good nutrition in care homes. One way of doing this is to tempt appetites with tasty morsels of well-prepared and attractively presented food. The best diet is useless if the food is not eaten.

Fresh ingredients of the highest quality are fundamental to all good dishes. If possible, choose the plumpest prawns, the sweetest fruit, the ripest cheeses, the tastiest herbs, the most succulent meat, the freshest fish and the crispest vegetables. Buying produce locally and in season ensures the best flavours. Using fresh ingredients also minimises the need for over-cooking and heavy sauces. The recipes we've included don't need complicated cooking methods, and allow the fresh, simple taste to shine through.

A balanced diet

As no single food provides all the nutrients our bodies need to be healthy and to function efficiently we provide a range of foods throughout the day that offer all the required nutrients and are cooked in a variety of ways to provide a balanced diet.

The foods should include

- Proteins for growth and repair, found in meat, poultry, fish, eggs, cheese, pulses, soya and nuts.
- Fat for energy. Some fats are not as good as others. Avoid saturated fats, which are usually solid at room temperature, as they can clog the arteries. Fats are found in cheese, eggs, milk, yoghurts oily fish and nuts. Oily fish is a great source of omega 3 and should be eaten at least twice a week to help keep joints pain free from arthritis and for preventing coronary heart disease.
- Carbohydrates, also for energy, include starches, sugars and fibre. Potatoes, pasta, bread and cereals all provide starch. Sugar is found in cakes, biscuits and fruit. Fibre is needed for good bowel health and is found in cereals and wholegrain foods.
- Vitamins are essential for all body processes. A, D, E and K are fat soluble so can be stored in the body, but the rest are water-soluble so must be eaten regularly to maintain a sufficient supply.
- Minerals are needed in different ways. Calcium and phosphorous are needed to maintain healthy bones. Iron is needed for the formation of red blood cells and is often deficient in those over 65. Iron-rich foods include: liver, kidneys, sardines, radishes, watercress, oatmeal, butter milk and spinach.

There are supplements that will provide vitamins and minerals, but the best source is always from the food we eat. Some foods are packed with vitamins and minerals that will enhance an individual's diet and ensure people get the recommended 5-a-day portions of vegetables and fruit.

Malnutrition in older people

Malnutrition is an imbalance of nutrients, which causes measurable adverse effects on tissue, body function and clinical outcomes. People over 65 are more at risk of malnutrition and this increases with age. Those over 80 are at risk of not being able to recover from malnutrition.

Causes of malnutrition?

- Older people tend to eat less, as their appetite can decrease with age, particularly if they also become less active.
- Eating is a social activity and if it is not enjoyable, appetite may diminish.
- Often, not enough care is given to individual likes and dislikes.
- Depression
- Problems with chewing and swallowing.
- The use of multiple medications may prevent absorption of nutrients.
- Not wanting to be a burden and ask for different foods that can be eaten more easily (e.g. finger foods).

Problems caused

- Impaired wound healing
- Loss of muscle strength
- Tendency to get infections and prolonged recovery time.
- Pressure sores
- Increase in falls
- Inactivity
- Mood shifts
- Confusion
- Lack of self-esteem

Suggestions

- Offer a balanced diet
- Listen to likes and dislikes
- Plan menus that include everyone's tastes
- Make dining an enjoyable social activity
- Get everyone involved
- Ensure that mealtimes are unrushed – remember who you are cooking for.
- Record any weight changes regularly and find ways of tempting even the tiniest appetite – for example, give a few mouthfuls of tasty nutritious food every few hours for those with little appetite.
- Treat those requiring feeding, or with special diets, with respect and dignity.
- Provide lovely nutritious food.

For those with dementia

When a person has dementia, food choices are often associated with meals they used to enjoy in the past, or made according to colour, texture and enhanced flavours. It is important not to make choices for people and not to limit the choice of food. Don't be afraid to try something new – the person will soon let you know if they don't like it!

The consequences of dietary imbalance or poor nutrition are well known. However, the changes that take place as dementia progresses will affect a person's relationship with food. These changes will vary in type and severity, depending on the type of dementia and the effect it has for the individual.

Consequences of not improving nutrition for the person with dementia are:

- Decrease in physical and emotional health
- Increased weight with loss of mobility
- Dehydration and constipation
- Poor wound healing, increased risk of infection, lethargy
- Reduced mobility
- Reduced ability to concentrate
- Reduced motivation
- Increased dependency on others

Finger Foods

Some people with dementia may become frustrated with trying to use cutlery or may not be able to settle for long enough to eat a meal in the dining room. Finger foods could be the ideal solution. They are served in bite-sized portions and can be picked up easily and eaten without the need for cutlery.

Benefits of finger foods:

- Easy to eat – ideal for those who cannot manage cutlery.
- Help preserve independence at mealtimes and boost self-esteem.
- Provide in-between meal nutrition.
- May help recover eating skills.
- Can be eaten at person's own pace.
- May renew interest in food and stimulate the appetite.
- Improve food intake and leave less waste.
- Allow greater choice.
- Give freedom to eat as desired.

How can we do this?

- Have bowls of fresh fruit or vegetables prepared and cut around the home, topping up and refreshing as required.
- Make smoothies and fruit and vegetable juice drinks every day.
- Show prepared food to residents so that they can make their choice. Let them smell it. Those with dementia may have forgotten what fish or chicken looks like – this will remind them what they like to eat.
- Make plenty of finger foods with a high protein content.
- Those with dementia are usually very active and use up many more calories than others so ensure they receive sufficient calories.
- Have plenty of nutritious snacks around for people to help themselves.
- As taste is often affected make sure that the food is tasty enough.
- Make sure that there is plenty to drink and that you monitor how much liquid is consumed.
- Offer a second helping of everything.
- Make sure that the food is served at the right temperature.
- Help with eating where necessary, but do this respectfully and discreetly

Smoothies & juices
for taste and health

What nicer way to enjoy a whole range of nutrients and ensure good hydration than a lovely fresh fruit juice or smoothie on a hot summer afternoon?

When residents are not interested in eating we can often tempt them with a lovely tasty vitamin and mineral filled drink.

Prepare a few different smoothies and juices for people to try; it stimulates taste buds and is very enjoyable. By adding certain foods you can supplement the diet well. For example cranberries are great for the urinary tract, flaxseed oil helps arthritic joints, blackcurrants are rich in vitamin C and strawberries are a great source of Vitamin C, iron and antioxidants. The list is endless, so experiment and discover favourite combinations.

Here are a few examples of ones we have developed:-

THE BOOSTER

2 bananas
2 carrots
½ pineapple
½ chopped fresh ginger

Blend well and serve with ice.
Great for digestion!

Serves 4

CONTAINS
Beta-carotene
Folic acid
Vitamin C
Magnesium
Manganese
Phosphorous
Potassium
Sodium
Sulphur

SUMMER SPECIAL

½ Melon
2 bananas
4oz strawberries

Blend and serve immediately.

Serves 4

MEMORY LANE MOMENT

100g (3½oz) silken tofu
2 bananas
1 small mango
2 soft pears

Blend and serve.

Serves 4

CHELSEA CREAM

1 small mango
2 bananas
4 fl oz plain yoghurt

Blend and serve.

Serves 4

THE RUNAROUND

4 sticks celery
2 carrots
small bunch watercress
¼ teaspoon freshly chopped ginger
1 tablespoon flaxseed oil
4 fl oz orange juice

Blend and serve.

Serves 4

A special book

This is a cookbook with a difference – wholesome food for every occasion, to suit all ages, styles and tastes, devised by people who are passionate about food. Barchester Healthcare residents, who have included the stories behind their particular choices, contribute many of the recipes. We have also included some of our chefs' recipes, which are regular favourites in their homes, as well as a few from the 2006 Barchester Chef competition held at Westminster College and judged by Paul Rankin and chef lecturers from the college. For each recipe we have outlined the nutritional values and the way in which they have been developed so that they are imaginatively served, nutritionally sound and include fresh ingredients.

Cooking for older people

Barchester Healthcare is renowned for the quality of services provided for residents. Whether it is the environment, the décor, the care, or the dining experience, great pride is taken in delivering excellent standards in everything. One of our greatest passions is food, and we want to ensure that residents enjoy not only the food but also the whole dining experience and to look forward to delicious homemade cakes, pastries and biscuits with their tea and coffee. We want our residents to be part of the planning process, by discussing their preferences with our chefs and in some cases even taking part in the cooking.

In 2005 the Barchester Chef Academy was set up. At the Academy, chefs are trained to cook, plan menus and balance the nutritional aspects of special diets with fresh seasonal ingredients. The chefs are expected to talk to residents about their individual tastes and dietary requirements as well as eating and swallowing difficulties. They make sure that residents are tempted to eat, even when their appetites diminish. In addition to discussing dishes with residents – and sometimes their relatives – we aim to ensuret that residents and their guests can enjoy the same food, by producing dishes that suit everyone and then substituting ingredients to meet particular requirements. Chefs at Barchester care homes sometimes make an event of taster sessions, when residents can try a new dish before it goes on the menu.

The inspiration for this book came from the first Barchester Chef Academy programme. As part of this programme, each chef was charged with devising and cooking a special recipe for one of their residents. Further inspiration came from the Barchester Chef 2006 Competition, the theme of which was 'Fine Dining Around the World'. There were some amazing entries: a trip on the Orient Express, dinner at Raffles in Singapore, the Darlin' Buds of May, the Titanic and many more. The spirit of each event was combined resident and staff involvement. Residents enjoyed making decorations, hats, menus and even some of the food for the events. The menus, tested out on residents many times prior to the finals, were so inspirational that we decided to put some of them into this book.

Why this book?

We have produced this book for a number of reasons:

- We want people to see how passionate we are at Barchester about the food we provide for residents, to share our enthusiasm for good food, and to share ideas and good practice.

- We want people to see that food for older people and those in care homes doesn't have to be bland and unappetizing, and that even those who have special dietary requirements can be offered interesting menus.

- We want to provide sound information to those of you cooking at home for older relatives and friends, and encourage you to prepare dishes that are adventurous as well as being suitable for their particular needs.

- We want to emphasize the importance of the whole dining experience as a pleasant social event, whether at home or in residential care.

And we want everyone to try our recipes and enjoy the experience!

And we want everyone to try our recipes and enjoy the experience!

Soups & Starters

The recipes we've included don't need complicated cooking methods, and allow the fresh, simple taste to shine through.

Soups have been enjoyed for centuries, from wholesome minestrone to lighter, more delicate broths. Soups are healthy, wholesome, and nutritious, and it's amazing how easily these can be turned from starters and snacks into a substantial meal and served with fresh, home-made bread – a veritable feast!

Soups are the basis of many of the diets in our homes so we have included some of our residents' favourites, along with ideas to make them even more interesting and nutritious.

The stockpots we used to have in hotels, restaurants, and even in some of your homes, have long gone. Sadly, re-heating foods causes too many food safety issues. The traditional stockpot sat on the stove for months, simmering away daily, producing lovely flavours and great bacteria! Stock powder or stock cubes are often more salty than flavoursome, so minimise their use where possible. Making fresh stock takes time, but gives a fabulous flavour. It's definitely worth the effort.

Colourful, light, tasty salads start a meal off well. Nutritious and attractive, they lead beautifully into the next course, awakening taste buds in readiness for the dishes that follow.

Many of the dishes in this chapter can be adapted to be served as substantial main courses or delightful supper dishes with a little bit of creativity.

Scotch Broth

This nutritious broth was chosen by Helen Thom from Glasgow, who enjoys it enormously.

INGREDIENTS	SERVES 4	SERVES 10
dried peas	25g/1oz	65g/2½oz
barley	25g/1oz	65g/2½oz
carrot	25g/1oz	65g/2½oz
turnip	25/1oz	65g/2½oz
small leek	1	2
shin of beef	100g/3½oz oz	250g/8oz
beef stock	1 litre/2 pints	litres/3½ pints

salt and freshly ground pepper
small parsley sprig, chopped, to garnish

METHOD

1 Soak the peas and barley overnight in cold water.
2 Peel and finely dice the vegetables into 5-mm/¼-in cubes.
3 Simmer the beef in the stock for 1 hour or until tender. Remove from the stock, cut into 1-cm/½-in cubes and return to the stock.
4 Drain the peas and barley and add to the stock then cook for 30–40 minutes.
5 Add the remaining vegetables, season, and simmer for 1 hour.
6 Sprinkle with chopped parsley and serve with freshly baked bread.

Chef's tip: Add other vegetables for a less traditional broth if you want to ring the changes.

NUTRITIONAL INFORMATION

Typical Values Per Portion
Energy 374 K J / 88 Kcal
Protein 9.1 g
Carbohydrate 8.5 g
(of which sugars) (1.0) g
Fat 2.0 g
(of which saturates) (0.6) g
Sodium 1.1 g
Fibre 1.2 g
Folate 5.32µg

Sweet Potato & Coconut Soup

Chef's tip: For a spicier version, stir in a little curry paste and chopped fresh coriander, to taste, and serve with warmed naan bread. For a creamier version, use full fat coconut milk.

This fabulous, high-energy soup is full of good ingredients and is popular at any time of year.

INGREDIENTS	SERVES 4	SERVES 10
butter	25g/1oz	50g/2oz
onion, chopped	1 small	1 large
sticks celery, chopped	2	5
sweet potato, peeled, cut into chunks	400g/13oz	1kg/2lb
vegetable stock	500ml/18fl oz	1.5 litres/2½ pints
coconut milk	200ml/7fl oz	500ml/18fl oz
salt and freshly ground black pepper		
desiccated coconut, plus extra to garnish	25g/1oz	50g/2oz
chopped fresh chives, to garnish		
a little paprika, to garnish		

METHOD

1 Heat the butter in a saucepan until just melted. Add the onion and celery and fry gently for 5 minutes until softened. Add the potato and cook for 5 more minutes.

2 Stir in the stock and coconut milk, season and bring to the boil. Cover and simmer for 30 minutes until the vegetables are tender.

3 Purée in a liquidiser or food processor, in batches, until smooth. Return to the pan. Stir in the desiccated coconut and reheat.

4 Ladle into bowls, then garnish with a little desiccated coconut, some chopped chives, and a little paprika.

NUTRITIONAL INFORMATION

Typical Values Per Portion
Energy 1699 K J / 409 Kcal
Protein 5.3g
Carbohydrate 25.0g
(of which sugars) (11.7) g
Fat 32.0g
(of which saturates) (26.0) g
Sodium 0,6g
Fibre 0.4g
Folate 28.25µg

Watercress Soup

Chef's tip:

This refreshing

soup is also great

served chilled in

the summer.

Watercress soup is a traditional soup, with some recipes dating back many centuries. This delicious soup may contribute to the daily requirements of vitamins and minerals.

INGREDIENTS	SERVES 4	SERVES 10
tbsp oil	1	3
onion, chopped	1	2
sticks celery, chopped	6	1 head
butter	50g/2oz	100g/3½oz
flour	25g/1oz	65g/2½oz
bunches watercress	6	12
vegetable or chicken stock	1 litre/2 pints	2 litres/3½ pints
tbsp cream	2	100ml
salt and freshly ground black pepper		
sprigs of watercress, to garnish		

METHOD

1 Heat the oil in a large pan. Sweat the onion and celery until tender.

2 Add the butter to the pan and melt. Stir in the flour to make a paste. Cook through then gradually add the stock. Bring to the boil ensuring that there are no lumps.

3 Add the watercress stalks and allow to simmer for 5–10 minutes.

4 Blanch the watercress leaves in boiling water for 20 seconds and then cool under cold water.

5 Strain the leaves and place into the blender with the ingredients from the pan and process until smooth. Return to the pan to heat through, season, and stir in the cream.

6 Garnish with sprigs of watercress.

**NUTRITIONAL
INFORMATION**
Typical Values Per Portion
Energy 615 K J / 148 Kcal
Protein 3.0g
carbohydrate 7.3g
(of which sugars) (2.4) g
Fat 11.9g
(of which saturates) (7.1) g
Sodium 0.6g
Fibre 0.4g
Folate 28.38µg

Minestrone Soup

This lovely, wholesome soup is great served with an olive ciabatti bread.

Chef's tip: Substitute tinned tomatoes for fresh if you are short of time.

INGREDIENTS	SERVES 4	SERVES 10
potato	75g/3oz	200g/7oz
carrots	75g/3oz	200g/7oz
swede	75g/3oz	200g/7oz
butter	50g/2oz	200g/7oz
medium onions, finely chopped	1	2
stalks celery	2	4
cloves garlic, finely chopped	2	2
vegetable stock	1 litre/1¾ pints	litres/3½ pints
tomatoes, skinned and deseeded	200g/7oz	400g/13oz
bunch basil, finely chopped	small	small
raw spaghetti broken into 2.5-cm/1-in pieces	50g/2oz	150g/6oz
frozen peas	25g/1oz	50g/2oz
canned kidney beans	25g/1oz	50g/2oz
salt and freshly ground black pepper		
grated Parmesan cheese, to serve		

METHOD

1 Prepare the potatoes, carrot, and swede by peeling and dicing into ½-in/1-cm dice.
2 Melt the butter in a large saucepan and sweat the onions until golden brown.
3 Add the potatoes, carrot, swede, celery, and garlic. Cook until soft.
4 Add the stock, tomatoes, and half the basil.
5 Bring to the boil and simmer for 20 to 30 minutes.
6 Add the spaghetti and cook for a further 15 minutes.
7 Add the peas and kidney beans and return to the boil.
8 Season and sprinkle with the remaining chopped basil.
9 Serve with grated Parmesan cheese.

NUTRITIONAL INFORMATION

Typical Values Per Portion
Energy 971 K J / 232 Kcal
Protein 7.8g
carbohydrate.26.8g
(of which sugars) (7.5) g
Fat 10.4g
(of which saturates) (5.6) g
Sodium 1.1g
Fibre 0.9g
Folate 18.25µg

Tomato & Basil Soup

Chef's tip:

If you are concerned about saturated fat levels, use 1 tbsp olive oil instead of the butter for frying and swirl in a little fromage frais instead of double cream at the end.

The rich, warming flavours of this soup make it a particular favourite for any occasion.

INGREDIENTS	SERVES 4	SERVES 10
butter	25g/1oz	65g/2½ oz
onion, chopped	1	2
sticks celery, chopped	2	5
carrot, diced	1	2
tomatoes, skinned and diced	500g/1lb	1.25kg/3lb
tbsp tomato purée	1	2
vegetable stock	600ml/1 pint	1.5 litres/2½ pints
demerara sugar	1 tsp	2 tsp
balsamic vinegar	2 tsp	5 tsp
double cream	4 tbsp	10 tbsp
bunch basil, finely chopped	small	large
salt and freshly ground black pepper		
few fresh basil leaves, to garnish, optional		

METHOD

1 Heat the butter in a saucepan, add the onion, celery, and carrot and fry gently for 5 minutes until softened. Add the tomatoes and fry for 5 more minutes.

2 Stir in the tomato purée and stock, season and bring to the boil. Add the chopped basil. Cover and simmer for 15 minutes.

3 Reserve a spoonful of the vegetables and purée the rest of the vegetables and stock in a liquidiser or food processor until smooth. Blend in batches if necessary. Return to the saucepan.

4 Stir in the sugar and vinegar and reheat the soup. Ladle into bowls, swirl the cream over the top, sprinkle over the reserved vegetables and garnish with basil leaves, if using.

NUTRITIONAL INFORMATION

Typical Values Per Portion
Energy 646 K J / 154 Kcal
Protein 2.7g
Carbohydrate 16.4g
(of which sugars) (14.9) g
Fat 8.7g
(of which saturates) (4.6) g
Sodium 1.2g
Fibre 0.6g
Folate 22µg

Baked Avocado Filled with Peppers

Chef's tip: This dish also works well with cheese or mushrooms instead of the peppers.

Avocados are almost a complete food, which means that they have most of the nutrients for a balanced diet. They are full of vitamin E, which is great for the skin. Peppers add vitamin C and the cheese adds protein – what a great dish!

INGREDIENTS	SERVES 4	SERVES 10
olive oil	1 tbsp	2 tbsp
small onion, finely chopped	½	1
red pepper, cored, deseeded, diced	½	1
tomatoes, peeled, deseeded, diced	2	5
ripe avocados	2	5
tbsp fresh or bottled lemon juice	2	5 tbsp
tbsp freshly grated Parmesan cheese	2	5 tbsp
salt and freshly ground black pepper		

METHOD

1 Preheat the grill to high.

2 Heat the oil in a frying pan, add the onion and red pepper and fry gently for 5 minutes until softened. Add the tomatoes and cook for 5 more minutes.

3 Halve each avocado, remove the stone and scoop out the flesh, reserving the avocado shells. Dice the flesh and toss in lemon juice.

4 Add the avocado to the tomato mixture, season, and warm through. Scoop the mixture into the avocado shells. Sprinkle with the Parmesan and cook under a hot grill until the cheese has just melted. Serve with a little salad garnish, if liked.

NUTRITIONAL INFORMATION

Typical Values Per Portion
Energy 1162 K J / 281 Kcal
Protein 5.2g
Carbohydrate 8.8g
(of which sugars) (6.8) g
Fat 25.0g
(of which saturates) (7.9) g
Sodium 0.3g
Folate 22.00µg
Fibre 0,9g

Stuffed Mushrooms

Chef's tip: Portabello mushrooms also work well in this recipe.

Dark, flat mushrooms have a much better flavour than the white, hothouse-grown ones, more commonly used these days. Try to find the soft, velvety looking ones – their flavour is superb. The cheese filling adds extra protein to this tasty dish.

INGREDIENTS	SERVES 4	SERVES 10
large flat mushrooms	4	10
olive oil	1 tbsp	2 tbsp
butter	25g/1oz	65g/2½ oz
medium tomatoes, skinned, deseeded, chopped	4	10
breadcrumbs	50g/2oz	125g/4 oz
chopped fresh parsley or basil	2 tbsp	5 tbsp
freshly grated Parmesan cheese	25g/1oz	65g/2 oz
salt and freshly ground black pepper		
sprigs of fresh parsley or basil to garnish, optional		

METHOD

1 Preheat the oven to 200°C/gas mark 6.

2 Remove the stalks from the mushrooms and chop finely. Peel mushrooms if needed, then brush the caps with oil. Set on a baking sheet, oiled side downwards.

3 Heat the butter in a frying pan, add the chopped mushroom stalks and fry for a few minutes until softened. Stir in the tomatoes, breadcrumbs, herbs, and seasoning.

4 Spoon the mixture on to the mushrooms and sprinkle with the Parmesan.

5 Bake for 10–15 minutes until piping hot and cheese is golden. Garnish with parsley sprigs if liked.

NUTRITIONAL INFORMATION

Typical Values Per Portion
Energy 684 K J / 163 Kcal
Protein 9.8g
Carbohydrate 1.6g
(of which sugars) (3.4) g
Fat 8.2g
(of which saturates) (4.7) g
Sodium 0.4g
Fibre 4.1g
Folate 38.59µg

Egg Mayonnaise

This is a really simple dish that can be made in a few minutes. It is easy to eat and always popular.

INGREDIENTS	SERVES 4	SERVES 10
eggs, hardboiled	8	20
lettuce leaves, finely shredded	4	10
mayonnaise	4 tbsp	10 tbsp
cayenne pepper, to sprinkle		
watercress, to garnish		

METHOD

1 Peel the eggs and halve them lengthways.
2 Divide the shredded lettuce among four small serving plates. Top with the eggs, yolks facing down. Coat with mayonnaise and sprinkle with a tiny pinch of cayenne pepper.
3 Garnish with watercress.

NUTRITIONAL INFORMATION

Using watercress for garnish adds extra iron to the diet.

Typical Values Per Portion
Energy 1082 K J / 261 Kcal
Protein 13.4g
Carbohydrate 1.4g
(of which sugars) (1.1) g
Fat 22.5g
(of which saturates) (4.8) g
Sodium 0.2g
Fibre 0.6g
Folate 69μg

Prawn Cocktail

Prawns used to be very expensive and only used for a very special treat. We have included this dish as it is a regular favourite for special events.

INGREDIENTS	SERVES 4	SERVES 10
tomato ketchup	1 tbsp	5 tbsp
mayonnaise	3 tbsp	10 tbsp
few drops vinegar		
lettuce, finely shredded	few leaves	½ lettuce
cooked, peeled prawns	150g/5oz	500g/1lb
lemon	1	3
pinch cayenne pepper		
slices brown bread, buttered	4	10

METHOD

1 Prepare the Marie Rose sauce by adding tomato ketchup to the mayonnaise with a few drops of vinegar to taste.

2 Place some shredded lettuce into the bottom of sundae glasses or Paris goblets. Take out one prawn per serving for garnish and divide the remaining prawns between glasses, placing on a bed of lettuce.

3 Spoon over enough Marie Rose sauce to cover the prawns.

4 Garnish with lemon wedges and the prawns held back for the garnish. Sprinkle a tiny pinch of cayenne pepper onto each prawn cocktail.

5 Serve with slices of thickly buttered, fresh brown bread.

Chef's tip: Using freshly cooked prawns makes this dish extra special, but frozen, thawed ones can be used instead. To make this into an attractive main course salad, increase the prawns to 100g/3½oz per person and add sliced tomatoes, cucumber, watercress, and hard-boiled eggs, quartered. Serve on a plate.

NUTRITIONAL INFORMATION

Typical Values Per Portion
Energy 1201 K J / 288 Kcal
Protein 12.0g
Carbohydrate 15.3g
(of which sugars) (3.1) g
Fat 19.9g
(of which saturates) (2.9) g
Sodium 965mg
Fibre 1.9g
Folate 20µg

Smoked Mackerel Salad

Chef's tip: This great salad can include so many different ingredients. For example, add sweetcorn, olives, asparagus, or grated carrot for extra nutrition and taste.

Mackerel is an oily fish, containing omega 3 fats. Eating oily fish once or twice a week is thought to help maintain a healthy cardiovascular system. Oily fish contains oils with vitamins A, D, E, and K throughout the flesh as opposed to white fish, which only has oils in the liver. Combined with the protein, vitamins, and minerals in the egg and vitamin C in the salad ingredients, this salad is a fabulously healthy meal.

INGREDIENTS	SERVES 4	SERVES 10
FOR THE SALAD:		
iceberg lettuce	½	1
beefsteak or ordinary tomatoes, deseeded and diced	200g/7oz	500g/1lb
cucumber, diced	¼	½
red onion, thinly sliced	½	1
watercress, rinsed, stems trimmed	40g/1½oz	100g/3½oz
small smoked mackerel fillets	4	10
hardboiled eggs, shelled	2	5
FOR THE DRESSING:		
olive oil	3 tbsp	6 tbsp
white wine vinegar	1 tbsp	2 tbsp
sugar	pinch of	½ tsp
dry mustard	pinch of	½ tsp
or Dijon	*1 tsp*	*1 tsp*
salt and freshly ground black pepper		
horseradish sauce, to serve		

NUTRITIONAL INFORMATION

Typical Values Per Portion
Energy 18780 K J / 453 Kcal
Protein 23.5g
Carbohydrate 4.3g
(of which sugars) (4.1) g
Fat 38.0g
(of which saturates) (7.7) g
Sodium 1.3g
Fibre 0.6g
Folate 14.69µg

METHOD

1 Tear the lettuce into bite-sized pieces and put into a salad bowl. Add the tomato, cucumber, onion, and watercress and toss gently together.
2 Peel the skin away from the mackerel and flake into chunky pieces. Cut the eggs into thin wedges and add both to the salad.
3 Put all the dressing ingredients into a screw-topped jar, shake together, then drizzle over the salad just before serving with a little dish of horseradish sauce.

Vegetable Dishes

As vegetables

are great

sources of

nutrients, it

is important

to make them

interesting

and tasty.

Vegetable dishes are often served with little imagination or flair. Plain carrots or leeks might be served when, with a little thought, they could become buttered carrots with tarragon, or leeks and courgettes with ginger.

Serve an appetizing range of fresh, colourful vegetables, steamed to maintain the maximum nutrients. We have called this a panache of vegetables; it sounds exciting and colourful. Brush them with butter and finely chopped parsley, or serve with a Hollandaise sauce to make them even more interesting.

Stir-frying vegetables also retains nutrients. Cooking for a shorter length of time, at a higher temperature, retains more of the colour too. Use your imagination and try new dishes; substitute some of the ingredients for different ones and supplement the vegetables with interesting herbs and spices.

Vegetable Gratin

A versatile dish to be served on its own or as an accompaniment to a roast dinner. It supplies vitamins, minerals and fibre in a delicious combination.

INGREDIENTS	SERVES 4	SERVES 10
cauliflower	1	2
small leeks	4	8 medium
chopped fresh tarragon	1 tsp	1 tbsp
Cheddar cheese, grated	3oz/75g	200g/7oz
salt and freshly ground black pepper		
butter, for greasing		
FOR THE MORNAY SAUCE	600ml/1 pint	1.25 litres/2¼ pints
flour	2oz/50g	
margarine or butter	2oz/50g	
onion studded with cloves	1	
pint milk, warmed	600ml/1	
Gruyère cheese	100g/31/2oz	
Parmesan	25g/1oz	
egg yolk	1	
pinch of cayenne pepper		

Chef's tip: Instead of using Cheddar for the sauce, try creamy ricotta or tangy blue Gorgonzola cheese instead.

METHOD

1 Trim the stem and remove the outer leaves of the cauliflower. Cut into florets and wash.

2 Trim the roots of the leeks, then cut off the dark green tops, leaving only the white and pale green parts. Slice lengthways within 2.5cm/1in of the root and wash under cold running water.

3 Cook in slightly salted boiling water or steam for no more than 15 minutes.

4 Meanwhile, make the sauce: melt the margarine or butter in a saucepan, stir in the flour and cook, stirring constantly, until the mixture comes away from the sides of the pan. Add the warmed milk gradually, mixing as it cooks, to make a smooth sauce. Add the studded onion, cover and simmer for 20 minutes, then remove the onion. Add the cheese, egg yolk and cayenne pepper, stirring well. Coat the vegetables with the sauce.

5 Drain well and place in a buttered ovenproof dish. Coat with the mornay sauce and add chopped tarragon.

6 Preheat the grill to high. Sprinkle the sauce with the grated cheese. Brown under the grill and serve.

NUTRITIONAL INFORMATION

Typical Values Per Portion
Energy 1369K J / 329 Kcal
Protein 117.8g
Carbohydrate 13.5g
(of which sugars) (8.1) g
Fat 22.6g
(of which saturates) (11.5) g
Sodium 0.6g
Fibre 1.0g
Folate 64µg

Sweet & Sour Red Cabbage

Chef's tip: Sweet and sour red cabbage is one of the few Vegetable dishes that is hard to overcook. It must be given plenty of time to allow the flavours to develop, so cook it very slowly.

Delicious as well as nutritious, this satisfying dish is a good source of folate (folic acid).

INGREDIENTS	SERVES 4	SERVES 10
olive oil	1 tbsp	3 tbsp
onion, finely chopped	1 medium	2
red cabbage, shredded	½ medium	1 large
cooking apples, peeled, cored, and diced	50g/2oz	125g/4oz
fresh root ginger, peeled and grated	1cm/½	2.5cm/1in
fennel seeds, crushed	½ tsp	1½ tsp
sugar	4 tsp	2 tbsp
ground cinnamon	pinch of	
vegetable stock	250ml/8fl oz	750ml/1¼ pints
vinegar	2 tbsp	50ml
butter	25g/1oz	75g/3oz
salt and freshly ground black pepper		

METHOD

1 Heat the oil in a large saucepan, add the onions, red cabbage, and apple and cook gently for 8–10 minutes.
2 Add the grated ginger, fennel, sugar, and cinnamon with the vegetable stock and the vinegar. Bring to the boil, simmer gently for 20–30 minutes until most of the liquid has evaporated and the vegetables are tender
3 Mix in the butter.
4 Season and serve.

NUTRITIONAL INFORMATION

Typical Values Per Portion
Energy 203 K J / 49 Kcal
Protein 1.0g
Carbohydrate 5.4g
(of which sugars) (4.8) g
Fat 2.5g
(of which saturates) (0.3) g
Sodium 0.5g
Fibre 1.5g
Folate 8.64µg

Vegetable Stir-Fry with Fine Egg Noodles

*Chef's tip:
Blanching the
vegetables cuts down
cooking time when
making this dish.
Otherwise, the stir-
fry method of cooking
might not be enough
to cook the vegetables
when cooking for
large numbers.*

Cooking vegetables quickly in hot fat retains much of the vitamin C and keeps the flavour. Most vegetables can be cooked in this way.

INGREDIENTS	SERVES 4	SERVES 10
red pepper, seeded and sliced	1	2
carrot, sliced thinly	1	2
sweetcorn	50g/2oz	125g
sesame oil	2 tbsp	4 tbsp
pak choi, shredded	1	2
root ginger, peeled and chopped	2.5cm/1in piece	10cm/4in
garlic clove, chopped	1	2 cloves
fine egg noodles	250g/8oz	600g/11/4lb
black bean sauce	1 x 300g jar	650g/11/2lb

METHOD

1 Blanch the pepper, carrot, and sweetcorn in boiling water for 2 minutes. Drain and refresh in cold water.

2 Heat half the oil in a large pan or wok and gently fry the pak choi with the ginger and garlic for 2–3 minutes.

3 Bring a pan of water to the boil, drop the noodles in and set aside.
Add the pak choi and blanched vegetable mixture to the pan or wok and continue to fry for 3–4 minutes.

5 Add the black bean sauce and bring to the boil. Meanwhile, drain the noodles, toss them in the remaining sesame seed oil, and arrange them onto a plate.
Spoon over the vegetable stir-fry, garnish with quarters of cherry tomatoes and chopped parsley and serve.

INFORMATION

Typical Values Per Portion
Energy 1047K J / 248 Kcal
Protein 11.9g
Carbohydrate 35.7g
(of which sugars) (13.8) g
Fat 6.4g
(of which saturates) (0.8) g
Sodium 2.1g
Fibre 2.8g
Folate 26.62µg

Potatoes, Peppers & Shallots Roasted with Rosemary

Chef's tip: For a special flavour add some cloves of garlic when roasting.

This interesting potato dish is tasty and nutritious and can be served with a wide range of foods, such as roasted meat, steak, and grilled fish. It is also a lovely supper dish, served with a green salad or coleslaw.

INGREDIENTS	SERVES 4	SERVES 10
waxy potatoes	500g/1lb	1.25kg/3lb
shallots	12	500g/1lb
sweet yellow peppers	2	5
olive oil	2 tbsp	4 tbsp
sprigs rosemary	2	6
salt and crushed black peppercorns		

METHOD

1 Preheat the oven to 200°C/gas mark 6.

2 Parboil the potatoes in their skins in boiling salted water for 5 minutes. Drain, – and when they are cool – peel them, and halve lengthways

3 Peel the shallots, allowing them to fall into their natural segments. Cut each sweet pepper lengthways into eight strips discarding the seeds and pith.

4 Cover the bottom of a shallow ovenproof dish with olive oil. Arrange the potatoes and peppers in alternating rows and stud with shallots.

5 Cut the rosemary sprigs into 2.5-cm/1-in lengths and tuck among the vegetables. Season the vegetables generously with salt and pepper, add olive oil and roast, uncovered, for 30–40 minutes or until all the vegetables are tender. Turn the vegetables occasionally to cook and brown evenly.

6 Serve hot, sprinkled with crushed peppercorns.

NUTRITIONAL INFORMATION

Typical Values Per Portion
Energy 758 K J / 180 Kcal
Protein 4.5g
Carbohydrate 24.6g
(of which sugars) (5.1) g
Fat 7.1g
(of which saturates) (0.9) g
Sodium 1.0g
Fibre 3.9g
Folate 15.30µg

Panache of Fresh Vegetables

Chef's tip: Almost any combination of vegetables can be used. In this selection, there is a range of tastes, colours, and textures.

Serving a range of colourful fresh seasonal vegetables not only looks and tastes good it is also full of vitamins, minerals, and fibre. Adding butter offers fat for warmth and energy. You can serve most vegetables this way. It makes excellent finger food too.

INGREDIENTS	SERVES 4	SERVES 10
baby carrots, halved	75g/3oz	200g/7oz
broccoli, cut into small florets	75g/3oz	200g/7oz
courgettes, cut into sticks	75g/3oz	200g/7oz
baby corn	75g/3oz	200g/7oz
mange tout	25g/1oz	65g/2½oz

FOR THE HERB BUTTER

butter	25g/1oz	65g/2½oz
chopped fresh tarragon, chives or parsley	2 tsp	4 tsp
finely grated lemon rind	1 tsp	2 tsp
salt and freshly ground black pepper		

METHOD

1 Cook the carrots in a steamer for 5 minutes.

2 Add the broccoli and cook for 2 minutes, then add the courgettes and corn and cook for 2 more minutes.

3 Add the mangetout and cook for 1–2 minutes until just tender. Meanwhile, beat the butter with the herbs, lemon rind, and seasoning.

4 Spoon the vegetables into a serving bowl and top with the herb butter. Serve immediately.

NUTRITIONAL INFORMATION

Typical Values Per Portion
Energy 58 K J / 14 Kcal
Protein 1.3g
Carbohydrate 1.6g
(of which sugars) (1.3) g
Fat 0.2g
(of which saturates) (nil)
Sodium trace
Fibre 0.4g
Folate 46.53µg

Sweet Potato & Feta Rösti

Chef's tip:
It is best to use
old potatoes, such
as Maris Piper or
Desiree for this dish
as the starchiness
helps bind the rösti
together. This makes
a great supper dish
served with a green
salad and herb
dressing or as an
accompaniment to a
meat or fish grill.

This dish is great served as an accompaniment or on its own as a supper dish or light lunch. It also goes well with a crisp green salad. Feta cheese has its own distinct creamy texture and salty flavour. It makes ideal finger food. Sweet potato is a good source of vitamin E, which helps to keep the skin healthy.

INGREDIENTS	MAKES 16 CAKES
old potatoes	250g/8oz
sweet potatoes	500g/1lb
onion	100g/4oz
fresh parsley, chopped	10g/½oz
fresh coriander, chopped	10g/½oz
cayenne pepper	pinch
feta cheese, cubed	100g/3½oz
butter, melted	25g/1oz
salt	
olive oil, for shallow frying	

METHOD

1 Preheat the oven to 150°C/gas mark 2.
2 Partly cook the old potatoes by blanching or steaming them for 15–20 minutes.
3 Grate both types of potato and the onion into a large bowl.
4 Add the herbs and season with cayenne pepper and salt.
5 Divide the mixture into 16 equal pieces.
6 Brush a 9-cm/3½-in round cake cutter with melted butter.
7 Place half a portion of mixture into the cutter and press down hard.
8 Add a few chunks of feta and top with the remaining portion of rösti mixture, press down hard. Place on a plate and remove the ring. Repeat with the remaining ingredients to make 16 cakes.
9 Shallow fry in a little olive oil until crispy on each side of the rösti. Finish by baking in the oven for 10 minutes.

NUTRITIONAL INFORMATION

Typical Values Per Portion
Energy 887 K J / 212 Kcal
Protein 6.2g
Carbohydrate 22.6 g
((of which sugars) (4.2) g
Fat 10.7g
(of which saturates) (6.8) g
Sodium 0.4g
Fibre 1.2g
Folate 21.06μg

Meat & Poultry

Buy good quality meat and poultry from a reputable butcher. Be sure to let him know if the meat, when cooked, wasn't the quality you had expected. You will soon find that you develop a mutually respectful relationship and the butcher will advise you of the best cuts, prices, and meats available.

Traditionally, many dishes in this chapter would have been prepared with cheaper, tougher cuts of meat than we have recommended. When meat was in short supply, we had to use every piece available, much of it with a high fat content and gelatinous sinews, which made great sauces and gravies. In days gone by, the stew we ate at supper might have been cooking all day, a necessity to make sure it was tender enough to enjoy.

We seem to have less time available to us and want things faster in the 21st century, yet expect our food to be just as tasty and wholesome as it was when our parents and grandparents cooked for us. The meat we buy now tends to be more appealing to the eye, with little or no fat. The downside is that leaner meat, with less fat and higher water content, can result in bland, tasteless dishes, so we have countered this with appropriate methods of cooking and the addition of herbs and spices to make the dishes as delicious as we remember them.

If you are not sure how to prepare the meat, the butcher will often do this for you. Watch and learn, as you will find that you can make a number of dishes for a fraction of the cost if you can prepare things yourself. For example, if you buy a whole chicken for chicken supremes, you can use the legs for another dish, and the stock and trimmings for a tasty soup, all at a fraction of the price of buying ready-cut supremes.

If you enjoy roasts, here's a secret that will impress your guests. Let the meat rest after roasting, for at least 20 minutes, before carving. This allows the sinews to relax and become really tender.

Fried Lamb's Liver & Bacon

Lamb's liver, which has a beautiful delicate flavour, is not always easy to purchase these days. This traditional dish is popular with older people and provides an excellent source of folate, protein, and many vitamins.

INGREDIENTS	SERVES 4	SERVES 10
lamb's liver	300g/10oz	1kg/2lb
plain flour	1oz/25g	3oz/75g
butter	50g/2oz	125g/4oz
streaky bacon	125g/4oz	300g/10oz
gravy	125ml/4floz	300ml/½ pint
salt and freshly ground black pepper		

METHOD

1 Skin the liver and remove any gristle. Cut into thin slices on the diagonal.
2 Coat the slices of liver in seasoned flour.
3 Heat the butter in a pan and fry the liver on both sides, taking care not to overcook as this will affect the texture of the offal
4 Preheat the grill to high and cook the bacon on both sides until crispy.
5 Serve the liver with the crisp bacon on top, with gravy, mustard mash, and fresh vegetables.

Chef's tip: Add fresh sage to the gravy, Serve with crisp Sweet Potato & Feta Rosti (page 36) instead of mustard mash.

NUTRITIONAL INFORMATION

Typical Values Per Portion
Energy 1136 K J / 273 Kcal
Protein 20.6g
Carbohydrate 0.9g
(of which sugars) (0.1) g
Fat 20.8g
(of which saturates) (9.7)g
Sodium 0.8mg
Fibre Ni
Folate 59µg

Chicken Pan Pie

Chef's tip: You can add a variety of ingredients to the chicken in step 4. Apricots add a lovely sweetness; sweetcorn is also tasty — or try prunes for a really special pie.

This tasty recipe was sent to us by a resident – it used to be a family favourite.

INGREDIENTS	SERVES 4	SERVES 10
butter	25g/1oz	75g/3oz
onion, chopped	1 small	2 medium
boneless, skinless chicken breasts, cut into cubes	4	10
red pepper, cored, deseeded and diced	1	2
green pepper, cored, deseeded and diced	1	3
button mushrooms, sliced	100g/3½oz	250g/8oz
stems fresh tarragon	2	5
white wine	4 tbsp	10 tbsp
salt and freshly ground black pepper		

FOR THE SAUCE:

butter	40g/1½oz	100g/3½oz
plain flour	40g/1½oz	100g/3½oz
milk	450ml/½ pint	1.25litres/2¼pints

FOR THE TOPPING:

fresh breadcrumbs	40g/1½oz	100g/3½oz
mature Cheddar cheese, grated	40g/1½oz	100g/3½oz

METHOD

1 Heat the butter in a frying pan, add the onion and chicken and fry for 5 minutes, stirring until lightly browned.

2 Stir in the peppers and mushrooms. Tear the tarragon into pieces and add with the wine and seasoning. Simmer for 5 minutes.

3 Meanwhile, make the sauce: heat the butter in a saucepan, stir in the flour, and cook for 1 minute. Gradually add the milk and bring to the boil, stirring until smooth and thickened. Season.

4 Stir the chicken mixture into the sauce then tip into a shallow ovenproof dish. Sprinkle with the breadcrumbs and cheese and bake at 190°C/gas mark 5 for 20 minutes until golden brown and the chicken is thoroughly cooked.

5 Serve with baby carrots or a selection of mixed vegetables.

NUTRITIONAL INFORMATION

Typical Values Per Portion
Energy 2684 K J / 641 Kcal
Protein 49.35g
Carbohydrate 37.9 g
(of which sugars) (11.8) g
Fat 32.0 g
(of which saturates) (17.4g)
Sodium 1.5g
Fibre 4.3g
Folate 33.46µg

Scottish Shepherd's Pie

Chef's tip:

Serve with

butter crushed

swede and

carrots

(see recipe

opposite).

We have included the Scottish version of a well-loved dish. Adding haggis increases the protein value as well as complementing the taste of other ingredients.

INGREDIENTS	SERVES 4	SERVES 10
FOR THE MEAT:		
dripping	25g/1oz	75g/3oz
medium onion, finely chopped	1	3
oil	1 tbsp	2 tbsp
minced lamb	450g/15oz	1kg/2lb
cooked haggis	100g/3½oz	250g/8oz
plain flour	1 tbsp	3 tbsp
bay leaves	2	5
sprigs of thyme	2	5
canned, chopped tomatoes	200g/7oz	500g/1lb
lamb stock	250ml/8fl oz	600ml/1 pint
Worcestershire sauce	2 tsp	5 tsp
salt and freshly ground black pepper		
FOR THE MASH:		
potatoes	750g/1½lb	1.75kg/4lb
milk, warmed	2 tbsp	150ml/¼ pint
butter	75g/3oz	175g/6oz
FOR THE BUTTER CRUSHED SWEDE AND CARROTS:		
carrots and swede, peeled and roughly chopped	500g/1lb	1.25kg/3lb
butter	2oz/50g	125g/4oz
salt and ground black pepper		

METHOD

1　In a large flameproof casserole dish, heat the dripping. Add the onion and cook for 5 minutes.
2　Meanwhile, in a large pan, heat the oil, fry the mince evenly and cook till brown. Add the cooked haggis.
3　Stir the onions in the casserole and add the flour. Mix well and add the bay leaf and thyme.
4　To the onion mixture, add the chopped tomatoes, stock (keep a little aside to deglaze the meat pan), and Worcestershire sauce.
5　Add the cooked mince to the casserole and then pour the stock mixture into the empty meat pan, scraping off any bits of mince left. Pour this into the meat mixture.
6　Bring to the boil, adding a pinch of pepper, cover and simmer for 45 minutes.
7　Cook the potatoes in boiling water until tender. Sieve the cooked potatoes into a bowl. Add the warmed milk, and butter, season and mash together.
8　Preheat the grill to medium. Spread the mash on top of the meat, smooth over and mark with a fork.
9　Grill for 10–15 minutes or until bubbling and browned.

METHOD FOR BUTTER CRUSHED SWEDE AND CARROTS:

1　Boil the carrots and swede together in a saucepan with salted water for 20 minutes until soft.
2　Drain well in a colander.
3　Put the carrots and swede back into the saucepan, add the butter and pepper and mash with a potato masher.
4　Serve immediately.

NUTRITIONAL INFORMATION

Typical Values Per Portion
Energy 000 K J / 666 Kcal
Protein 28.82g
Carbohydrate 8.5 g
(of which sugars) (1.0) g
Fat 2.0 g
(of which saturates) (42.77g)
Sugar 5.46g
Sodium 1466mg
Iron 5.56mg
Vitamin C 15.50mg
Folate 35.70µg
Fibre 3.35g

Lamb Biryani

If you don't

have a pestle

and mortar for

grinding the

spices, improvise

with a mug

and the end of a

rolling pin or, for

large amounts,

use a liquidiser.

Josephine Hamilton chose Lamb Biryani as one of her favourites after tastng it for the first time at her Care Home's International Food Day, when dishes from different countries were available for everyone to try.

INGREDIENTS	SERVES 4	SERVES 10
green cardamom pods	10	35
cloves	5	12
cinnamon stick, broken into small pieces	½	2 sticks
coriander seeds	1 tsp	2 tsp
chilli powder	½–1tsp	2 tsp
paprika	1 tsp	2 tsp
turmeric	1 tsp	2 tsp
fresh ginger, peeled and finely chopped	5-cm/2-in piece	10-cm/4-in piece
low fat natural yogurt	500g/1lb	1.25kg/3lb
salt	1 tsp	2 tsp
diced lamb	625g/1¼lb	1.5kg/3½lb
clarified butter	50g/2oz	125g/4oz
onion, finely chopped	1	2
cloves garlic, finely chopped	2	5
lamb stock	200ml/7fl oz	500ml/18fl oz
ground almonds	4 tsp	2 tbsp
medium mango, peeled and sliced	½	1
flaked almonds, lightly toasted	1 tbsp	2 tbsp
chopped fresh coriander	4 tsp	2 tbsp

NUTRITIONAL INFORMATION

Typical Values Per Portion
Energy 2282 K J / 546 Kcal
Protein 37.4g
Carbohydrate 26.6 g
(of which sugars) (23.9) g
Fat 32.3 g
(of which saturates) (15.4)g
Sodium 1.6g
Iron 4.11mg
Vitamin C 11.22mg
Fibre 1.3g
Folate 18.40µg

METHOD

1 Grind the spice pods and seeds as finely as possible using a pestle and mortar. Stir all the spices and salt into the yoghurt. Place the meat in a non-metallic dish and cover with the yogurt. Cover and leave to marinade overnight in the fridge.
2 Remove the meat from the marinade, and reserve the marinade.
3 Heat the clarified butter in a large saucepan and sweat the onions and garlic. Stir in the meat and brown slightly.
4 Add the marinade and stock to the pan.
5 Add the ground almonds, chopped mango, flaked almonds and coriander.
6 Bring to the boil, allow to simmer for 30–40 minutes until tender.
7 Serve with pilau rice, mango chutney, cucumber raita, and naan bread.

Beef, Barley &
Dijon Mustard Stew

Chef's tip:
Substitute some
of the stock for a
little red wine if
liked. This can also
be cooked in the
oven at 180°C/gas
mark 4 for 2 hours.
Pearl barley swells
as it stands, so if
you make this in
advance, you will
need to top up with
extra stock before
reheating.

We developed this interesting beef stew with barley to add to the protein content of the beef and to enhance the flavour. Beef has a much higher water content now than 30 or 40 years ago and many people find that this makes the flavour a little bland, so we have complemented it with other flavours in this dish.

INGREDIENTS	SERVES 4	SERVES 10
olive oil	1 tbsp	2 tbsp
large leek, chopped	1	2½
topside of beef, cubed	500g/1lb	1kg/2lb
parsnips, peeled and cubed	500g/1lb	1kg/2lb
tomatoes, peeled and chopped	500g/1lb	1kg/2lb
stalk celery, chopped	1	3
beef stock	600ml/1 pint	1.5 litres/2½ pints
Dijon mustard	1 tbsp	3 tbsp
pearl barley	100g/3½ oz	250g/8oz
fresh thyme or marjoram	few sprigs	few sprigs
(plus extra to garnish)		
salt and freshly ground black pepper		

NUTRITIONAL INFORMATION

Typical Values Per Portion
Energy 1380 K J / 328 Kcal
Protein 31.2g
Carbohydrate 23.6 g
(of which sugars) (7.4) g
Fat 11.7 g
(of which saturates) (3.0)g
Sodium 1.1g
Fibre 5.3g
Folate 44.82µg

METHOD

1 Heat the oil in a saucepan, add the leek and beef and fry over a high heat until the beef is evenly browned.
2 Stir in the remaining vegetables, stock, mustard, and barley. Add the herbs and seasoning and bring to the boil, stirring.
3 Cover and simmer for 1½ hours, stirring occasionally until the beef is tender. Top up with extra stock if needed.
4 Sprinkle with extra herbs to garnish and serve with Duchess potatoes (see opposite page).

Duchess Potatoes

INGREDIENTS	SERVES 4	SERVES 10
old potatoes	500g/1lb	1.25kg/3lb
butter	25g/1oz	65g/2½oz
egg yolk (optional)	1	2
salt and freshly ground black pepper		

METHOD

1 Preheat the oven to 200°C, gas mark 6.

2 Peel the potatoes and cut them into evenly sized pieces.

3 Boil in salted water for approximately 20 minutes until cooked.

4 Drain and return to the pan.

5 Add the butter and mash well. Add the egg yolk if using.

6 Put the mixture into a piping bag with 1cm/1/2in star nozzle.

7 Pipe 4cm/11/2in rosettes onto greased baking trays.

8 Place in the centre of the oven for 5-10 minutes or until golden brown.

Chicken Cacciatore

Chef's tip:

This great

dish can be

served with

rice or any

type of pasta.

This prize-winning recipe was created by chef Jane Ennis for a competition.

INGREDIENTS	SERVES 4	SERVES 10
chicken supremes	4	10
olive oil	1 tbsp	3 tbsp
mushrooms, finely chopped	125g/4oz	300g
medium onion, chopped	1	3
clove garlic, crushed	1	3
dry white wine	125ml/4fl oz	300ml/½ pint
white wine vinegar	1½ tbsp	3 tbsp
chicken stock	125ml/4fl oz	300ml/½ pint
fresh basil	1 teaspoon	2 tsp
dried marjoram	½ teaspoon	1 tsp
salt	½ teaspoon	1 tsp
pepper	large pinch of	large pinch of
can whole peeled tomatoes	425g/14oz	1kg/2lb
black olives, pitted and chopped	8	20
chopped fresh parsley	1 tbsp	2 tbsp
fresh basil leaves, to garnish		

METHOD

1 Rinse the chicken; drain and pat dry. Heat the oil in a large frying pan over a moderate heat. Add the chicken, cook for 8 minutes on each side until brown; set aside in a large saucepan.

2 Add the mushrooms and onion to the pan juices remaining in the frying pan. Cook and stir over a moderate heat for 5 minutes or until the onion is soft. Add the garlic and cook for 30 seconds. Add the wine vinegar, and cook over a moderate heat for 5 minutes or until the liquid is almost evaporated. Stir in the stock, basil, marjoram, salt and pepper. Remove from the heat.

3 Add the tomatoes, bring to the boil and cook for 2 minutes.

4 Pour the sauce over the chicken, bring to the boil, reduce the heat to low. Cover and simmer for 25 minutes or until the chicken is tender and cooked.

5 Add the olives and parsley to the sauce and stir well. Serve the chicken garnished with the basil.

NUTRITIONAL INFORMATION

Typical Values Per Portion
Energy 1621 K J / 388 Kcal
Protein 38.73g
Carbohydrate 8.5g
(of which sugars) (4.8) g
Fat 18.6 g
(of which saturates) (4.0)g
Sodium 1.7g
Fibre 1.7g
IFolate 25.26µg

Pheasant in Red Wine

Pheasant is a special treat for many when in season. It is low in fat and high in protein. It is easy to digest making it a great dish for all.

INGREDIENTS	SERVES 4	SERVES 10
olive oil	2 tbsp	6 tbsp
pheasant breasts	2	6
red onion, finely chopped,	1	2
red wine	300ml/½ pint	750ml/1¼ pints
balsamic vinegar	2 tbsp	5 tbsp
beef stock	3 tbsp	125ml/4fl oz
butter	15g/½oz	40g/1½oz
mushrooms, sliced	100g/3½oz	250g/8oz

METHOD

1 Heat the oil in a frying pan and add the pheasant breasts and red onion. Cook for 2–3 minutes until beginning to colour.
2 Add the red wine, balsamic vinegar, and stock, with the butter, and bring to the boil.
3 Allow to simmer for 15 minutes or until cooked through and reduced.
4 Sauté the mushrooms in a separate pan until just tender. Add to the sauce.
5 Serve the pheasant with the sauce drizzled over the top.

FOR THE STILTON CRUSHED POTATOES:

old potatoes	500g/1lb	1.25kg/3lb
butter, cubed	2oz/50g	125g/4oz
Stilton cheese, crushed	2oz/50g	125g/4oz

salt and freshly ground black pepper

METHOD

1 Cut the potatoes into evenly sized pieces.
2 Cook in a saucepan of boiling salted water for 20 minutes until soft.
3 Drain and return to the saucepan.
4 Add the butter and Stilton cheese.
5 Crush lightly with a fork, season, and serve.

Chef's tip: Serve with Stilton potatoes (see recipe below). Add a knob of butter to the sauce for an extra sheen.

NUTRITIONAL INFORMATION

Typical Values Per Portion
Energy 1843 K J / 442 Kcal
Protein 37.7g
Carbohydrate 3.6 g
(of which sugars) (2.6) g
Fat 25.2g
(of which saturates) (11.7)g
Sodium 0.6g
Iron 5.29mg
Vitamin C 0.673mg
Fibre 1.5g
Folate 24.50µg

Brisket of Beef with Spiced Plum Sauce

Chef's tip:

For a different

twist, marinate

the beef overnight

in brown ale or

red wine with

peppercorns, bay

leaves, and garlic.

Brisket of beef is a very traditional British dish. Long, slow cooking renders the meat tender and easy to eat. We have added a tasty plum sauce to make this a little more special and to aid digestion.

INGREDIENTS	SERVES 4	SERVES 10
brisket joint	1kg/2lb	2 kg
brown sugar	20g/¾oz	50g
olive oil	1 tbsp	2 tbsp
large onion, cut into 8 wedges	1	3
carrots, cut into chunks	2	5
clove garlic, finely chopped	1	3
beef stock	450ml/¾ pint	1 litre/1¾ pint
plum jam	1 tbsp	3 tbsp
red wine vinegar	1 tbsp	2 tbsp
five spice powder	½ tsp	1 tsp
bay leaves	2	5
salt and freshly ground black pepper		

METHOD

1 Rub the beef with the sugar and a little seasoning. Heat the oil in a flameproof casserole; add the beef and brown on all sides.

2 Add the onion, carrots, and garlic then pour in the stock. Add the jam, wine vinegar, spice powder, and bay leaves and bring the stock to the boil.

3 Cover and simmer gently for 2 hours, turning the beef from time to time and topping up with extra stock if needed.

4 Remove the meat from the pan once cooked and keep hot. Boil the stock rapidly to reduce by half then strain. Taste and correct the seasoning. Slice the beef thinly and serve with the braised vegetables. Mashed parsnips, and a steamed green vegetable of your choice. are also good with this dish.

NUTRITIONAL INFORMATION

Typical Values Per Portion
Energy 2692 K J / 648 Kcal
Protein 39.7g
Carbohydrate 11.1g
(of which sugars) (9.7) g
Fat 49.4g
(of which saturates) (18.8)g
Sodium 1.4g
Fibre 0.4g
Folate 9µg

Gammon Casserole

Chef's tip: Use fresh apricots when in season. Cook this in a preheated oven (180°C/ gas mark 4) for 30–40 minutes if preferred.

Mary Archer and her husband used to enjoy this tasty gammon casserole every week after shopping at the local market – it is still one of Mary's favourites.

INGREDIENTS	SERVES 4	SERVES 10
butter	25g/1oz	75g/3oz
thick gammon steaks	2	5
or gammon, fat and rind trimmed away, diced	*500g/1lb*	*1.25kg/3lb*
ground mixed spice or allspice	large pinch	
plain flour	2 tbsp	5 tbsp
ham or chicken stock	300ml/½ pint	750ml/1¼ pints
sweet or dry sherry	2 tbsp	5 tbsp
cranberry sauce	1 tbsp	3 tbsp
tomato purée	2 tsp	5 tbsp
slices fresh pineapple, peeled, cored and diced	2	5
canned apricot halves, thickly sliced	8	20
salt and freshly ground black pepper		

METHOD

1 Heat the butter in a frying pan, add the gammon and mixed spice and fry for 5 minutes, stirring.

2 Sprinkle in the flour then gradually mix in the stock. Stir in the sherry, cranberry sauce, tomato purée, and seasoning and mix well. Then add the pineapple and apricots. Cover and simmer gently for 15 minutes.

3 Serve in shallow bowls with mashed potatoes speckled with chopped parsley.

NUTRITIONAL INFORMATION

Typical Values Per Portion
Energy 1885 K J / 453 Kcal
Protein 26.5g
Carbohydrate 15.7g
(of which sugars) (7.9) g
Fat 30,7g
(of which saturates) (12.2)g
Sodium 4.6g
Fibre 1.3g
Folate 4.01µg

Chicken Breast with Sage, Onion & Cranberry

This is roast chicken with a difference. It combines all the traditional flavours of roast chicken, sage, and onion, but also adds a piquant cranberry taste. Apart from tasting great, cranberries are also extremely beneficial in keeping the urinary tract healthy.

INGREDIENTS	SERVES 4	SERVES 10
chicken breasts	4	10
onions, finely chopped	50g/2oz	125g/4oz
olive oil	2 tbsp	6 tbsp
breadcrumbs	100g/3½oz	250g/8oz
fresh sage, finely chopped	7g/½oz	15g/½oz
egg, beaten	1	2
rashers streaky bacon	4	10
butter	25g/1oz	65g/2½oz
flour	25g/1oz	65g/2½oz
chicken stock	600ml/1 pint	1.5 litres/2½ pints
cranberries	250g/8oz	625g/1¼lb
salt and freshly ground black pepper		

METHOD

1. Preheat the oven to 180°C/gas mark 4.
2. Slit each chicken breast lengthwise, but do not cut right through.
3. Make up the stuffing by gently frying the onions in half the oil, add the breadcrumbs and chopped sage. Season and bind with egg.
4. Divide the stuffing into four and fill the slit of each chicken breast. Wrap a rasher of bacon around each breast and brush with the remaining oil. Place the chicken in an oven tin and roast for 20–25 minutes.
5. Melt the butter in a saucepan, add the flour, and cook for 1 minute, stirring constantly. Gradually add the stock, stirring constantly. When thoroughly mixed, add the cranberries and cook over a gentle heat for 30 minutes. Season and pour over the chicken.
6. Serve with Duchess potatoes (page 49) and a panache of vegetables (page 36).

Chef's tip: Make sure that the chicken does not dry out in the oven. To prevent this, baste regularly with oil or any cooking juices. Serve with creamy mashed potatoes, buttered broccoli, and sweetcorn for a delicious and nourishing winter lunch.

NUTRITIONAL INFORMATION

Typical Values Per Portion
Energy 1834 K J / 437 Kcal
Protein 40.8g
Carbohydrate 25.7 g
(of which sugars) (3.6) g
Fat 19.0g
(of which saturates) (7.2)g
Sodium 0.1g
Fibre 1.9g
Folate 10µg

Fish & Shellfish

A few tips on buying fish: look for clear, bright, bulging eyes; if they are sunken, steer well clear.

Fish and shellfish are great sources of protein, and contain the sorts of oils that are good for you, together with many of the vitamins and minerals essential for the growth and repair of cells. They are also versatile in terms of cooking and very easy to digest.

Fresh fish has a shiny clear surface with a metallic glint – if it has an opaque film of mucus, don't buy it. The gills should be a bright red and the scales should be shiny and plentiful. Talk to your fishmonger, who will let you know what is good to buy and might offer suggestions for cooking. Fish should be eaten on the day you buy it.

Filleting, skinning, and boning can be done with speed and with little waste since the bones can be used to make a tasty fish stock. If you find the preparation daunting, you might prefer to buy fish ready prepared, but be aware that the costs are generally higher and it is less easy to determine how fresh the fish is.

Many people make the mistake of over-cooking fish. This can make it tasteless and chewy. Steaming is the best method of cooking for most fish. Tuna and salmon work well when lightly cooked, particularly when they have been caught the same day.

Many of our residents look forward to traditional fish and chips each Friday. For some, this has been a long tradition. Many will enjoy fish in batter, whilst others prefer to try a range of different fish dishes. This chapter shows how some of the traditional dishes, enjoyed since childhood, have been creatively updated to make new, exciting dishes to suit a range of tastes.

Citrus Salmon with Buttered Beetroot

This recipe is extremely nutritious. Salmon provides omega 3 fats and helps maintain the cardiovascular system. Eating vegetables in a variety of colours supplies a range of vitamins and minerals.

Chef's tip: Serve with buttered new potatoes.

INGREDIENTS	SERVES 4	SERVES 10
citrus fruit zest (lemon, lime, or orange, or a combination)	25g/1oz	65g/2½oz
fresh breadcrumbs	300g/10oz	750g/1½lb
butter, melted	200g/7oz	500g/1lb
flour	25g/1oz	65g/1½oz
salmon fillets or steaks, cut into 2.5 x 8-cm/1 x 3-in strips	500g/1lb	1.25kg/3lb
oil, for frying		
salt and freshly ground black pepper		

FOR THE BEETROOT:

	SERVES 4	SERVES 10
fresh beetroot	500g/1lb	1.5kg/3½lb
fresh parsley, finely chopped	1 tbsp	2 tbsp
butter, melted	25g/1oz	65g/1½oz

METHOD

1. Preheat the oven to 200°C/gas mark 6.
2. Place the zest, breadcrumbs, butter, and seasoning into a food processor and pulse until mixed. Season the flour.
3. Coat the salmon strips in seasoned flour and cover with the breadcrumb mixture.
4. Heat the oil in a frying pan, add the salmon strips, and cook for one minute on each side. Remove from the heat and spoon over any additional breadcrumb mixture.
5. Transfer to the oven and bake for 5 minutes.
6. Steam or boil the beetroot in their skins for 50–60 minutes or until cooked. Peel and dice when cool enough. Serve with the chopped parsley and melted butter.

NUTRITIONAL INFORMATION

Typical Values Per Portion
Energy 2563 K J / 614 Kcal
Protein 26.1g
Carbohydrate 43.1g
(of which sugars) (7.3) g
Fat 37.5g
(of which saturates) (16.3)g
Sodium 0.7g
Fibre 5.6g
Folate 1.93μg

Seafood Parcels
with Crème Fraîche & Dill

Seafood parcels are a delightful treat for suppertime, as a feature on a teatime buffet table, or as an unusual start to a special meal. They are very quick and easy to make and the salmon contains omega 3 oils. Eating oily fish such as salmon, once or twice a week is thought to help maintain a healthy cardiovascular system.

INGREDIENTS (MAKES 12 PARCELS)

100g/3½oz salmon fillet
½ lime, juice only
100g/3½oz prawns
100g/3½oz scallops
2 tbsp chopped fresh chives
pinch cayenne pepper, optional
500g/1lb filo pastry (sheets)
50g/2oz butter, melted
4 tsp chopped fresh dill
4 tbsp reduced-fat crème fraîche
salt and freshly ground black pepper
a few chives, lightly blanched in boiling water, for serving

METHOD

1 Rinse the fish in cold water, drain well, sprinkle with the lime juice, and poach in the microwave for 4–5 minutes until tender.
2 Leave the fish to cool, then remove the salmon skin and any bones, flake into pieces. Roughly chop the prawns and scallops. Mix with the chives, seasoning, and cayenne, if using.
3 Preheat the oven to 190°C/gas mark 5.
4 Cut the filo pastry sheets into 10-cm/4-in squares. Brush one square with melted butter and place another square on top at a slight angle to the first, then brush with butter.
5 Spoon some of the fish mixture onto the filo square. Pull the corners of the pastry up and over the filling, pinch together and tie with string. Place on a baking sheet. Repeat with the remaining pastry and filling.
6 Brush the outside of the parcels with any remaining butter, then bake for 10–15 minutes until golden brown.
7 Meanwhile, stir the chopped dill into the crème fraîche and season.
8 Remove the string from the pastry parcels and replace with the blanched chives. Arrange on serving plates with spoonfuls of the crème fraîche. Serve with salad.

Chef's tip: These look great on a buffet table – for a birthday party or special event. You can use blanched leek strips instead of string to tie the parcels. Keep the filo pastry covered with a damp cloth until needed.

NUTRITIONAL INFORMATION

Typical Values Per Portion
Energy 654 K J / 157 Kcal
Protein 7.3g
Carbohydrate 7.6g
(of which sugars) (0.4) g
Fat 10.8g
(of which saturates) (5.9)g
Sodium 0.3g
Fibre 0.1g
Folate 14.12µg

Salmon Fishcakes

Chef's tip: Serve with a tomato and sweet chilli relish or make your own by stirring diced tomatoes into sweet chilli sauce.

This appetizing recipe is the favourite of Miss Eva Langdon, who was a teacher all her working life.

INGREDIENTS	SERVES 4	SERVES 10
FOR THE FISHCAKES:		
salmon	500g/1lb	1.25kg/3lb
potatoes, cut into chunks	625g/1¼lb	1.5kg/3½lb
egg yolks	2	5
chopped fresh parsley	3 tbsp	7 tbsp
lemon, grated rind only	1	2
salt and freshly ground black pepper		
FOR THE COATING:		
plain flour	2 tbsp	5 tbsp
egg, beaten	1	2
fresh breadcrumbs	75g/3oz	200g/7oz
sunflower oil	3 tbsp	7 tbsp
lemon wedges, to garnish		

METHOD

1 Cut the salmon into three pieces and steam for 10–12 minutes until just cooked and the fish flakes easily when pressed with a knife. Meanwhile, cook the potatoes in a saucepan of boiling water, or in the base of the steamer, for 15 minutes until tender.

2 Drain and mash the potatoes with the egg yolks. Stir in the parsley, lemon rind, and seasoning.

3 Remove the skin from the salmon, then flake into chunky pieces, discarding any bones. Stir into the potatoes.

4 Divide the mixture into eight equal pieces, leave to cool, then pat into cakes.

5 Put flour on one plate, egg on a second, and breadcrumbs on a third. Coat the fishcakes in flour, then egg, and finally breadcrumbs. Chill until ready to cook.

6 Preheat the oven to 180°C/gas mark 4. Heat 2 tbsp oil in a large frying pan, add as many fishcakes as will fit in the pan, and fry until golden brown on both sides. Transfer to the oven to keep warm. Add the remaining oil to the pan and cook the remaining fishcakes.

7 Transfer to serving plates, garnish with lemon wedges, and serve with rocket salad and spoonfuls of tomato relish, if liked.

NUTRITIONAL INFORMATION

Typical Values Per Portion
Energy 3129 K J / 744 Kcal
Protein 45.7g
Carbohydrate 79.9g
(of which sugars) (3.7) g
Fat 26.9g
(of which saturates) (5.3) g
Sodium 0.6g
Fibre 6.0g
Folate 26.25µg

Parma Ham wrapped Salmon with White Wine & Cucumber Sauce

Chef's tip:

Try this with

thin slices

of pancetta

instead of the

Parma ham

for a change.

This rather special recipe is full of goodness, with added iron and folate (folic acid) in the spinach.

INGREDIENTS	SERVES 4	SERVES 10
pieces salmon fillet	4 x 100g/4oz	10 x 100g/4oz
chopped fresh parsley	2 tbsp	5 tbsp
fresh thyme leaves	2 tsp	5 tsp
Parma ham	4 slices	10 slices
butter (plus extra for greasing)	50g/2oz	125g/4oz
shallots, finely chopped	25g/1oz	65g/2½oz
dry white wine	150ml/¼pt	400ml/14fl oz
piece cucumber, finely diced	5cm/2in	10cm/4in
lemon, grated rind only	1	2
olive oil	1 tbsp	2 tbsp
baby spinach leaves	375g/12oz	1kg/2lb
salt and freshly ground black pepper		

METHOD

1 Preheat the oven to 200°C/gas mark 6.

2 Rinse the salmon with cold water, drain well, then sprinkle with half the parsley, all the thyme, and a little seasoning. Wrap with Parma ham and put into a buttered roasting tin.

3 Roast the salmon for 10–12 minutes or until the fish flakes easily when pressed with a knife.

4 Meanwhile, heat the butter in a saucepan, add the shallots and fry gently for 5 minutes until softened. Add the wine and simmer for 5 minutes until reduced by half. Stir in the cucumber, lemon rind, and remaining parsley.

5 Heat the oil in a wok, add the spinach, and stir fry for 2 minutes until just wilted. Season and spoon into the centre of four serving plates. Arrange the cooked salmon on top and spoon the cucumber sauce around the edge of the plate. Serve immediately.

NUTRITIONAL INFORMATION

Typical Values Per Portion
Energy 2011 K J / 484 Kcal
Protein 32.9g
Carbohydrate 4.0 g
(of which sugars) (3.6) g
Fat 29.9 g
(of which saturates) (10.4)g
Sodium 0.7g
Fibre 0.4g
Folate 36.90µg

Stir-Fry Prawns with Mangetout & Sesame

Chef's tip: Do not overcook the stir-fry or the vegetables will lose their vibrant colours and crispiness.

Stir-frying vegetables retains many more of the nutrients than boiling in water, as many minerals are water soluble. The vegetables are cooked more quickly, the flavour is better and the appearance is great. Try cooking almost any variety of vegetables in this way.

INGREDIENTS	SERVES 4	SERVES 10
sunflower oil	1 tbsp	2 tbsp
small onion, chopped	1	2
each of green, red, and yellow peppers, deseeded, chopped	½	1
sesame oil	2 tsp	5 tsp
peeled raw jumbo prawns, defrosted if frozen, rinsed	400g/13oz	1kg/2lb
clove garlic, finely chopped	1	3
chopped fresh root ginger	1 tsp	2 tsp
mangetout	150g/5oz	400g/13oz
head pak choi, thickly sliced	1	2
beansprouts, rinsed	150g/5oz	400g/13oz
fish sauce	2 tsp	5 tsp
soy sauce	2 tsp	5 tsp
lime, juice only	1	2
fresh coriander, torn into pieces	small bunch	large bunch
sesame seeds	15g/½oz	40g/1½oz

NUTRITIONAL INFORMATION

Typical Values Per Portion
Energy 683 K J / 162 Kcal
Protein 24.0g
Carbohydrate 5.7g
(of which sugars) (4.7) g
Fat 4.8g
(of which saturates) (0.6)g
Sodium 1.6g
Fibre 1.9g
Folate 31.14µg

METHOD

1 Heat the sunflower oil in a wok, add the onion and chopped peppers, and stir fry for 5 minutes until softened.
2 Add the sesame oil, then the prawns, garlic, and ginger, stir fry for 3–4 minutes until the prawns have turned pink all over.
3 Add the mangetout, pak choi, and beansprouts, stir fry for 1 minute then mix in the fish sauce, soy sauce, and lime juice. Stir fry for 1–2 minutes until the pak choi leaves have just wilted. Sprinkle with the coriander and sesame seeds and serve with rice.

Cracking Fillet of Cod

Chef's tip:

Take care not

to overcook this

simple, tasty

dish as white

fish is delicate

and dries out

quickly.

Connie Lawson lived with her grandmother when she was young and remembers spending hours cooking with her. She became a mother's help and stayed with one family for 52 years, becoming their cook. This recipe was one that she was often asked to make for family and visitors.

INGREDIENTS	SERVES 4	SERVES 10
small fillets of cod or haddock	4 x 125g/4oz	10 x 125g/4oz
butter (plus a little for greasing)	15g/½oz	25g/1oz
low fat natural yoghurt	125g/4oz	250g/8oz
pink peppercorns, roughly crushed	1 tsp	1 tbsp
salt		
mature Cheddar cheese, grated	25g/1oz	70g

METHOD

1 Preheat the oven to 170°C/gas mark 3.

2 Rinse the fish with cold water, drain well, and arrange in a single layer in a buttered shallow ovenproof dish. Spoon the yogurt over the top so that the fish is completely covered then sprinkle with the peppercorns, a little salt, and the cheese.

3 Bake uncovered for 15–20 minutes until the cheese is golden and the fish flakes easily when pressed with a knife.

4 Transfer to plates and serve with halved, grilled cherry tomatoes, halved, steamed sugar snap peas, garden peas and new potatoes.

NUTRITIONAL INFORMATION

Typical Values Per Portion
Energy 597 K J / 142 Kcal
Protein 21.5g
Carbohydrate 4.7g
(of which sugars) (1.0) g
Fat 2.0 g
(of which saturates) (Nil)
Sodium 0.1g
Fibre Nil
Folate 51.60µg

Haddock Florentine

Chef's tip:

Any fish or

shellfish can be

used in this dish

to add variety.

Fresh fish with a cheese sauce and spinach offers a wide range of nutrients and tastes delicious. This dish is high in protein and fat, so ideal for a high energy diet. It is also very easy to eat and digest.

INGREDIENTS	SERVES 4	SERVES 10
FOR THE FISH:		
haddock fillets	4 x 100g/4oz	10 x 100g/4oz
milk	150ml/¼ pint	300ml/½ pint
butter, cubed	25g/1oz	75g/3oz
FOR THE CHEESE SAUCE:		
butter	50g/2oz	125g/4oz
flour	50g/2oz	125g/4oz
mustard powder	pinch	pinch
milk	500ml/18 fl oz	1 litre/1¾ pints
onion studded with cloves	1	2
bouquet garni	1	2
Gruyère cheese, grated	50g/2oz	125g/4oz
double cream	1 tbsp	3 tbsp
cayenne pepper	pinch	pinch
cooked spinach, drained	200g/7oz	500g/1lb
Parmesan cheese, grated	25g/1oz	65g/2½oz
salt and freshly ground black pepper		

METHOD

1 Preheat the oven to 150°C, gas mark 2.
2 Place the haddock in a shallow ovenproof dish, cover with the milk and butter, season, and bake for 20 minutes. Drain and reserve the milk.
3 To prepare the cheese sauce, melt the butter in saucepan, add the flour and mustard powder, cook for 1 minute stirring constantly.
4 Gradually add the reserved and extra milk, bringing to the boil after each addition and stirring constantly to ensure that there are no lumps.
5 Add the onion and bouquet garni and simmer for 20 minutes.
6 Remove the onion and bouquet garni. Add the cheese, cream and cayenne pepper, mix well and check for seasoning.

NUTRITIONAL
INFORMATION
Typical Values Per Portion
Energy 2072 K J / 496 Kcal
Protein 44.1g
Carbohydrate 17.1 g
(of which sugars) (8.0) g
Fat 27.9g
(of which saturates) (16.6)g
Sodium 0.5g
Fibre 0.2g
Folate 30.31µg

7 Place the cooked spinach onto an ovenproof dish. Add the drained, cooked haddock. Preheat the grill to high.

8 Coat with cheese sauce and sprinkle with Parmesan.

9 Brown under the grill and serve with Marquise potatoes (see below) and a medley of fresh vegetables.

Marquise Potatoes

INGREDIENTS	SERVES 4	SERVES 10
old potatoes	500g/1lb	1.25kg/3lb
onions	25g/1oz	65g/2½oz
peeled, deseeded and chopped tomatoes	50g/2oz	125g/4oz
salt and freshly ground black pepper		

METHOD

1 Preheat the oven to 200°C, gas mark 6.

2 Peel the potatoes and cut them into evenly sized pieces.

3 Boil in salted water for approximately 20 minutes until cooked.

4 Meanwhile, finely slice the onions and cook in a little oil until transparent. Add the chopped tomatoes and keep warm.

5 Drain the potatoes and return to the pan. Add the butter and mash well. Add the egg, if using.

6 Put the mixture into a piping bag with a 1cm/1/2in star nozzle and pipe small nests of potato onto a greased baking tray.

7 Place in the centre of the oven for 5-10 minutes or until golden brown. Fill with the tomato mixture when cooked.

Chef's tip:

Make sure the fish is well drained before coating with sauce or it will be too runny.

Fishy on a Dishy

Chef's tip:

Almost any

fish can be

used in this

dish. It is

particularly

good with

oily fish.

This is a great recipe for those who live by the sea and can buy really fresh fish. The chef who sent us this recipe developed it after watching the TV serial 'When the Boat Comes In', in which *Fishy on a Dishy* was the theme tune. It is a very tasty and nutritious dish.

INGREDIENTS	SERVES 4	SERVES 10
FOR THE TOMATO SAUCE:		
olive oil	1 tbsp	2 tbsp
onion, finely chopped	1	2
cloves garlic, finely chopped, optional	1–2	5
tomatoes, peeled and diced	500g/1lb	1.25kg/3lb
caster sugar	1 tsp	2 tsp
salt and freshly ground black pepper		
FOR THE FISH:		
mackerel fillets	4 x 75g/3oz	10 x 75g/3oz
trout fillets	4 x 100g/3½oz	10 x 100g/3½oz
FOR THE TOPPING:		
butter	25g/1oz	65g/2½oz
fresh breadcrumbs	50g/2oz	150g/5oz
hardboiled eggs, peeled and chopped	2	5
chopped fresh parsley	2 tbsp	5 tbsp

METHOD

1 Preheat the oven to 200°C/gas mark 6.
2 Make the tomato sauce by heating the oil in a saucepan, add the onion and garlic, if using, and fry for 5 minutes until softened and just beginning to turn golden. Stir in the tomatoes, sugar, and seasoning. Cover and simmer for 10 minutes.
3 Place a mackerel fillet in a shallow ovenproof dish skin side down. Place a trout fillet on top of each mackerel fillet with the skin side facing upwards.
4 Pour the tomato sauce over, loosely cover with foil, and bake for 10 minutes.
5 Meanwhile, heat the butter in a frying pan, add the breadcrumbs and cook, stirring, until golden brown and crisp. Stir in the eggs and parsley.
6 Remove the foil from the fish and sprinkle the crumb mixture over the top of the fish and tomato mixture. Bake for 5 more minutes until the fish flakes easily when pressed with a knife. Serve with new potatoes and mixed steamed vegetables.

NUTRITIONAL INFORMATION

Typical Values Per Portion
Energy 2644 K J / 633 Kcal
Protein 50.7g
Carbohydrate 22.6g
(of which sugars) (10.2) g
Fat 37.8g
(of which saturates) (10.6)g
Sodium 1.0g
Fibre 0.4g
Folate 43.84µg

Craster Kedgeree

Named after a famous fishing village, this tasty dish is a favourite at Harton Grange Care Home near the Lancashire coast, where fresh fish is readily available and is always popular.

INGREDIENTS	SERVES 4	SERVES 10
smoked haddock	300g/10oz	700g/1lb/10oz
basmati rice	150g/5oz	400g/13oz
sunflower oil	1 tbsp	2 tbsp
onion, finely chopped	1	2
mushrooms, chopped	125g/4oz	250g/8oz
butter	25g/1oz	75g/3oz
mild curry paste or powder	4 tsp	3 tbsp
crabmeat	250g/8oz	625g/1¼lb
hardboiled eggs, peeled, chopped	4	10
chopped fresh parsley	3 tbsp	7 tbsp
lemon wedges, to garnish		

METHOD

1 Poach the smoked haddock in a frying pan of simmering water for 8–10 minutes until just cooked. Drain and cool.

2 Add the rice to a saucepan of boiling water, cook for 10 minutes until just tender. Drain, rinse with cold water and drain again.

3 Rinse and dry the frying pan, add the oil, and fry the onion for 5 minutes until softened and just beginning to brown. Stir in the mushrooms and fry for 2 minutes.

4 Stir in the butter and curry paste, cook for 1 minute, then mix in the rice.

5 Flake the haddock into pieces, discarding the skin and bones. Add to the rice mixture with the crabmeat, eggs, and parsley. Heat through, garnish with lemon wedges, and serve immediately.

NUTRITIONAL INFORMATION

Typical Values Per Portion
Energy 2462 K J / 589 Kcal
Protein 57.6g
Carbohydrate 17.0g
(of which sugars) (3.9) g
Fat 32.3g
(of which saturates) (12.7)g
Sodium 1.5g
Fibre 2.3g
Folate 45.10µg

Quick Meals

You could

experiment

with flans

and quiches,

adding a

huge range of

vegetables and

interesting

ingredients.

Sandwiches or beans on toast do not offer sufficient nutrients to encourage good health. At suppertime, a meal rich in protein will help to keep you satisfied for longer. Residents in care homes often choose to eat at 5 or 6 o'clock, which means that they will require a snack later in the evening. Providing sandwiches at suppertime often results in two bread-based snacks, which is not only dull and uninteresting but does not provide the nutrients required. So, provide delicious tasty supper dishes, full of nutrients.

To avoid meat twice in one day, you might prefer to provide cheese or fish dishes. Pulses are also ideal for supper dishes and a good source of protein. You could experiment with flans and quiches, adding a huge range of vegetables and interesting ingredients.

Don't forget that using the right combination of ingredients – soup and lovely home-made bread – can make a highly nutritious supper dish.

Corned Beef, Thyme & Sweet Potato Pie

This recipe came from a lady who used to cook this dish for her husband just after the War, when fresh meat was difficult to get. We have used sweet potato in the pie, an ingredient not generally available in those days. Sweet potato makes a nutritious alternative to traditional mashed potato and gives the dish a lovely sweet flavour that contrasts with the savoury beef.

Chef's tip: Serve with maple roasted parsnips and carrots.

INGREDIENTS	SERVES 4	SERVES 10
oil	1 tbsp	3 tbsp
medium onions, finely chopped	2	5
plain flour	1 tbsp	3 tbsp
sprigs of thyme	2	5
beef stock	300ml/½ pint	500ml/18fl oz
cherry tomatoes	100g/3/½ oz	250g/8oz
Worcestershire sauce	2 tsp	5 tsp
corned beef, cut into 2cm/¾in cubes	450g/1lb	1kg/2lb
salt and freshly ground black pepper		
sweet potato, peeled and chopped	500g/1lb	1kg/2lb
floury potatoes, peeled and chopped	200g/7oz	450g/15oz
butter	75g/3oz	200g/7oz
double cream	2 tbsp	5 tbsp

METHOD

1 Heat the oil and cook the onions in a large flameproof casserole dish.
2 Stir in the flour. Mix well and add the thyme and the beef stock.
3 Add the tomatoes and Worcestershire sauce to the onion mix.
4 Add the corned beef and season well.
5 Preheat the oven to 200°C/gas mark 6.
6 Cook all the potatoes in boiling water until tender. When cooked, sieve and put into a bowl. Add the butter and cream. Mix well.
7 Spread the mash on top of the meat, smooth over and mark with a fork.
8 Cook for 10–15 minutes until bubbling and browned.

NUTRITIONAL INFORMATION

Typical Values Per Portion
Energy 2959 K J / 709 Kcal
Protein 33.7g
Carbohydrate 46.0g
(of which sugars) (13.0) g
Fat 43.4 g
(of which saturates) (21.8) g
Sodium 1.9g
Fibre 2.2g
Folate 20µg

Cornish Pasties

Chef tip: This traditional dish is always popular and easy to eat.

Cornish pasties were originally the working lunch of tin miners. They had a savoury filling in one side and sweet apples in the other. The pastry was made very thick so that the pasty would stay warm until lunchtime!

MAKES 8 PASTIES

FOR THE SHORTCRUST PASTRY:
500g/1lb plain flour, plus a little for rolling out
pinch salt
225g/8oz lard, hard margarine, or butter, or a combination of these, diced
cold water, to bind

FOR THE FILLING:
350g/12oz rump steak
200g/7oz potato, peeled, sliced, and finely diced
200g/7oz swede, peeled, sliced, and finely diced
1 small onion, finely chopped
salt and freshly ground black pepper
20g/¾oz butter
1 tbsp plain flour
1 egg, beaten

METHOD

1 Put the flour and salt into a bowl, add the fat, and rub in with fingertips or an electric mixer to form fine crumbs. Mix in enough water to bind together and lightly knead to a smooth ball. Don't over work the pastry, cover and chill for 20 minutes before rolling.

2 Trim any fat off the steak and cut into small dice. Mix together the meat and vegetables in a bowl with a little seasoning.

3 Preheat the oven to 220°C/gas mark 7.

4 Roll out the pastry thinly on a lightly floured surface and cut out 8 17-cm/6½-in circles, re-rolling pastry trimmings as needed.

5 Divide the filling between the pastry circles, dot with the butter and a light sprinkling of flour (this helps to make the gravy). Moisten the edge of the pastry with water or beaten egg then fold in half. Press the edges together to seal well, then flute between finger and thumb.

NUTRITIONAL INFORMATION
Typical Values Per Portion
Energy 2105 K J / 504 Kcal
Protein 17.0g
Carbohydrate 45.6g
(of which sugars) (3.0) g
Fat 28.2g
(of which saturates) (12.2g
Sodium 0.4g
Fibre 1.2g
Folate 14.98µg

Chef's tip: Substitute parsnip for some of the potato for a change.

6 Transfer the pasties to a lightly greased baking sheet, brush with egg. Then make small hole on top for the steam to escape.
7 Bake at 220°C/gas mark 7 for 20 minutes, then reduce the temperature to 170°C/gas mark 3 for 20–30 minutes. Cover with foil after 15 minutes if the pasties seem to be browning too quickly.
8   Serve warm with salad.

Cumberland Sausage with Colcannon Mash

Chef's tip: Serve the Cumberland sausage on a bed of colcannon mash with rich onion gravy.

This classic British regional sausage is made with chopped pork, herbs and spices, and is traditionally served coiled.

INGREDIENTS	SERVES 4	SERVES 10
olive oil	1 tbsp	3 tbsp
Cumberland sausages	4	10

FOR THE COLCANNON MASH:

	SERVES 4	SERVES 10
potatoes, chopped	1kg/2lb	2.25kg/5lb
cabbage, finely shredded	450g/15oz	1.25kg/3lb
leeks, finely sliced	2	5
milk	150ml/½ pint	375ml/12fl oz
butter	100g/3½oz	250g/8oz
salt and freshly ground black pepper		

METHOD

1 Preheat the oven to 180°C/gas mark 4.
2 Brush the sausages with the oil, place in a roasting tin and cook for 30–35 minutes.
3 Boil the potatoes until cooked, drain and return to the pan.
4 Cook the cabbage for 2–3 minutes in salted boiling water until just cooked, drain and refresh under cold water. Rinse the leeks thoroughly.
5 Put the milk and butter in a pan and bring to a simmer, add the sliced leeks and simmer for 8–10 minutes.
6 Mash the potatoes.
7 Combine all the colcannon ingredients and stir on a low heat.
8 Season with salt and pepper. Divide the mash among 4 plates and top with the cooked sausages to serve.

NUTRITIONAL INFORMATION

Typical Values Per Portion
Energy 20674K J /495 Kcal
Protein 14.9g
Carbohydrate 44.4g
(of which sugars) (10.8) g
Fat 28.71 g
(of which saturates) (16.1)g
Sodium 0.8g
Fibre 2.9g
Folate 92.168µg

Toad in the Hole with Onion & Cider Gravy

Toad in the hole has plenty of carbohydrates for energy. It has protein in the milk, eggs, and meat for growth and repair. It can also be eaten as finger food and is great for many diabetics. Always a popular choice.

INGREDIENTS	SERVES 4	SERVES 10
FOR THE BATTER:		
plain flour	250g/8oz	500g/1lb
pinch of salt		
large eggs	2	5
milk	600ml/1 pint	1 litre/1¾ pints
chopped sage	1 tbsp	2 tbsp
chopped parsley	1 tbsp	2 tbsp
chopped chives	1 tbsp	2 tbsp
FOR THE TOAD:		
pork and apple sausages	8	20
olive oil	4 tbsp	100ml/3½fl oz
large portabella mushroom, sliced	4	10
cherry tomatoes	300g/10oz	625g/1¼lb
FOR THE GRAVY:		
butter	40g/1½oz	100g/3½oz
onion, sliced	1	2
flour	20g/½oz	50g/2oz
beef or chicken stock	600ml/1 pint	1 litre/1¾ pint
dry cider	300ml/½ pint	500ml/18fl oz
Worcester sauce	1 tbsp	2 tbsp
soy sauce	1 tbsp	2 tbsp
salt and freshly ground black pepper		

NUTRITIONAL INFORMATION

Typical Values Per Portion

Energy 2894 K J / 692 Kcal
Protein 28.1g
Carbohydrate 62.5g
(of which sugars) (14.9) g
Fat 35.1g
(of which saturates) (16.4) g
Sugar 13.59g
Sodium 2.1g
Iron 3.85mg
Vitamin C 45.49mg
Folate 23.36µg
Fibre 2.70g

METHOD

1 Preheat the oven to 220°C, gas mark 6.
2 For the batter, sieve the flour and salt into a large mixing bowl. Add the eggs and milk gradually until it's all incorporated into a smooth batter. Stir in the herbs and allow to rest.
3 For the gravy, heat the butter in a pan and fry the onions until soft and well browned. Add the flour and stir well.
4 Gradually add the stock and cider, whisking continuously. Add the Worcestershire sauce and soy sauce and season to taste.
5 Leave to simmer, stirring occasionally until lightly thickened.
6 While the gravy is cooking, prick the sausages all over with a fork. Pour half of the olive oil into a roasting tin and place over a high heat.
7 Add the sausages and brown. Remove from the tin and set aside.
8 Add the mushrooms and fry until soft. Return the sausage to the tin with the cherry tomatoes and remaining olive oil. Place in the oven for 5 minutes.
9 Stir the batter mix and pour quickly into the tin.
10 Return to the oven and bake for 35–40 minutes until puffed and golden brown.
11 Serve with the onion and cider gravy.

Chef's tip: As an alternative to gravy, replace the cider with wine and add 25g/1oz tomato puree and 50g/2oz sliced mushrooms to the sauce.

Creative Pizzas

Chef's tip: You can rub in 50g/2oz butter to the flour to enrich the pizza base if you like.

Residents love 'Pizza Day', when they are involved in either making their own pizzas or choosing their own toppings.

NUTRITIONAL INFORMATION

Typical Values Per Portion

Energy 1272 K J / 303 Kcal
Protein 15.52g
Carbohydrate 30.3g
(of which sugars) (3.0) g
Fat 13.3g
(of which saturates) (7.9g
Sodium 0.5g
Fibre 0.7g
Folate 59µg

INGREDIENTS: MAKES 8 LARGE OR 20 SMALL INDIVIDUAL PIZZAS

FOR THE PIZZA BASE:
pinch sugar
50g/2oz fresh yeast
1.5 litres/2½ pints warm water
good pinch salt
1kg/2lb strong flour

FOR THE TOMATO SAUCE:
500g/1lb onions, finely chopped
1kg/2lb tomatoes
1 litre/1½ pints vegetable stock
½ tsp dried or 1 tsp fresh oregano
dash of Worcestershire sauce

IDEAS FOR PIZZA TOPPINGS:
cheese, grated
mushrooms, sliced
onions, sliced
tomatoes, sliced
peppers, chopped
olives, pitted
sweetcorn
prawns
tuna fish, canned
anchovies
pepperoni
bacon, chopped and fried
pineapple, chopped
ham, chopped

METHOD
1 Prepare the pizza base by mixing the sugar and yeast together with a little of the warm water (if it is too hot, it will kill the yeast, and if it is too cold it will rise very slowly).
2 Add the salt to the flour.
3 When the yeast has begun to froth add it to the flour with the rest of the water.
4 Mix well, then knead for 5–10 minutes on a floured board.
5 Place in clean bowl, cover with a damp cloth, and leave to rise in a warm place until doubled in size.
6 To make the sauce melt the butter and cook the onions in a large pan for 5–10 minutes, or until transparent.
7 Add the remaining sauce ingredients to the pan, bring to the boil, and simmer for 5–10 minutes.
8 Turn the dough out onto a floured board again and knead. This breaks the air bubbles into smaller ones resulting in a more even pizza.
9 Shape into individual pizzas or large ones to cut up and place on baking sheets.
10 Allow to rise again until doubled in size. Preheat the oven to 200°C/gas mark 6.
11 Cover with tomato sauce and add your chosen toppings.
12 Cook for 20–25 minutes.

Chef's tip: Allow residents to choose their own toppings, or they make like to make an individual pizza. It's great fun for all.

Thai Beef Salad

Chef's tip: This is also delicious served as a starter — either make the full amount to serve eight, or try half the amount for four servings. If you are lucky enough to have roast beef left over from the Sunday joint, use this instead of the steak.

Although there are only a few salads in this book, we have tried to offer a range that demonstrates how interesting, imaginative and nutritious they can be. This delightful Thai salad has lovely flavours to delight any palate and a range of nutrients to help maintain good health.

INGREDIENTS	SERVES 4	SERVES 10
sirloin steaks	2 x 200g/7oz	5 x 200g/7oz
olive oil	1 tbsp	2 tbsp

FOR THE DRESSING:

spring onions finely chopped	2	5
lemon grass, finely chopped (optional)	1 stem	2 stems
chopped fresh coriander leaves	4 tbsp	10 tbsp
fresh chopped mint leaves	1 tbsp	2 tbsp
lime, juice only	1	2
fish sauce	1 tbsp	2 tbsp
sweet chilli sauce	1 tbsp	2 tbsp

FOR THE SALAD:

iceberg lettuce	½	1
cucumber, thinly sliced	¼	½
tomatoes, halved, sliced	2	5
spring onions, cut into thin strips	2	5
fresh coriander leaves, torn into small sprigs	small bunch	large bunch

NUTRITIONAL INFORMATION

Typical Values Per Portion
Energy 962 K J / 231 Kcal
Protein 18.8g
Carbohydrate 2.1g
(of which sugars) (1,9) g
Fat 16.4g
(of which saturates) (6.9) g
Sodium 0.1g
Fibre 0.7g
Folate 41.40µg

METHOD

1 Brush the steaks with the oil and fry in a preheated frying pan, or under the grill, until medium rare, or medium if preferred. Allow to stand for 5 minutes.
2 Meanwhile, mix all the dressing ingredients together in a bowl.
3 Tear the lettuce into bite-sized pieces and put into a salad bowl with the cucumber, tomatoes, spring onions, and coriander leaves. Toss gently together, then divide between four serving plates.
4 Trim the fat away from the steaks, then cut into thin slices. Arrange on top of the salad, drizzle with the dressing, and serve while the steak is still warm.

Stovies

Chef's tip: This classic dish is usually cooked on the stove. Cooking it in the oven with layers of potatoes gives a great finish and flavours are retained more effectively.

A traditional Scottish dish of layered meat and potatoes – a great all-in-one meal for a winter's day!

INGREDIENTS	SERVES 4	SERVES 10
beef stewing steak	500g/1lb	1kg/2lb
large onion, sliced	1	2
old potatoes	500g/1lb	1kg/2lb
good beef stock	500ml/18floz	1.5 litres/2½ pints
small sprig of thyme (optional)	1	3
salt and freshly ground black pepper		

METHOD

1 Preheat the oven to 150°C/gas mark 2.
2 Layer the beef, onions and sliced potatoes ending with potatoes on the top, in an ovenproof dish.
3 Season and add the stock and thyme.
4 Cook for 1½–2 hours or until the meat is tender.
5 Serve with fresh root vegetables or braised red cabbage.

NUTRITIONAL INFORMATION

Typical Values Per Portion
Energy 1133 K J / 268 Kcal
Protein 32.5g
Carbohydrate 2.7g
(of which sugars) (5.3) g
Fat 5,3g
(of which saturates) (2.0) g
Sodium 1.0g
Fibre 2.6g
Folate 29.68µg

Leek & Brie Tart

This tasty and nutritious dish, with plenty of protein, is a favourite lunch or suppertime dish.

INGREDIENTS	SERVES 4	SERVES 10
shortcrust pastry	175g/6oz	400g/13oz
small leeks	8	20
eggs	2	5
grated nutmeg		
Brie cheese, sliced	25g/1oz	65g/2½oz

FOR THE SAUCE:

butter	15g/½oz	40g/1½oz
plain flour	15g/½oz	40g/1½oz
milk and leek cooking stock	150ml/½ pint	400ml/14fl oz
salt and freshly ground black pepper		

METHOD

1 Preheat the oven to 200°C/ gas mark 6.

2 Roll the pastry out and use it to line a 18-cm/7-in flan tin. Bake blind for 20 minutes.

3 Return to the oven for 5 minutes then leave to cool. Reduce the oven temperature to 190°C/gas mark 5.

4 Cut off the green part of the leeks and tie the white parts into bundles. Cook in boiling water or steam for 10 minutes. Reserve the cooling liquid. Squeeze dry and slice thinly.

5 To make the sauce, melt the butter in saucepan, add flour and cook through. Gradually, add the milk and leek stock, stirring constantly to ensure that there are no lumps.

6 Remove from the heat and beat in the eggs, salt and pepper, and nutmeg to taste.

7 Put a layer of sauce into the cooled pastry case top with the leeks, then the remaining sauce.

8 Top with the Brie and bake for 20 minutes or until golden.

Chef's tip:
Try a range of different fillings for other interesting tarts. Try mushrooms, olives, or peppers for variety.

NUTRITIONAL INFORMATION

Typical Values Per Portion
Energy 1469K J / 352 Kcal
Protein 10.9g
Carbohydrate 25.9g
(of which sugars) (4.8) g
Fat 22.8g
(of which saturates) (9.3) g
Sodium 0.6g
Fibre Nil
Folate 19.20μg

Vegetable, Bean & Saffron Risotto

Chef's tip:

This lovely, tasty dish is soft to eat and can be adapted for most diets.

This dish can be adapted for both vegetarians and vegans by omitting the pancetta and Parmesan respectively. By combining different varieties of beans along with rice, you can ensure that vegetarians get a good range of nutrients and flavours.

INGREDIENTS	SERVES 4	SERVES 10
olive oil	2 tbsp	4 tbsp
pancetta	50g/2oz	125g/4oz
medium onion, finely chopped	1	2
cloves garlic, finely chopped	2	5
parsnip, cut into 1cm/½in cubes	100g/3½oz	250g/8oz
courgettes, cut into 1cm/½in cubes	100g/3½oz	250g/8oz
arborio rice	100g/3½oz	125g/4oz
saffron	good pinch	3 pinches
vegetable stock	500ml/18fl oz	1.5 litres/2½ pints
frozen peas	50g/2oz	125g/4oz
canned black eyed beans	500g/1lb	1.25kg/3lb
fresh parsley	2 tbsp	6 tbsp
grated Parmesan cheese, to serve		

NUTRITIONAL INFORMATION

Typical Values Per Portion
Energy 2287 K J / 542 Kcal
Protein 35.1g
Carbohydrate 73.7 g
(of which sugars) (8.6) g
Fat 11.8 g
(of which saturates) (2.6) g
Sugar 8.60g
Sodium 296mg
Fibre 2.7g
Folate 418.47µg

METHOD

1 Heat the oil in a large pan and add pancetta, onion and garlic, cook until the onion is soft.
2 Add the cubed parsnips and courgettes. Cook for 5 minutes.
3 Add the rice and mix well. Add the saffron.
4 Combine the wine andthe vegetable stock in a jug.
5 Add the stock gradually, stirring all the time, ensuring that the liquid is fully absorbed before adding more. This will take about 30 minutes.
6 When the liquid is fully absorbed, check whether the rice is cooked – it might need a little more stock. Cook until absorbed.
7 Add the frozen peas, black eyed beans, and parsley. Cook through.
8 Serve immediately, sprinkled with Parmesan.

Crab & Baby Corn Rissoles

Chef's tip:
Serve with a
delicious mango
salsa (see recipe
opposite).

These rissoles make great finger food and taste wonderful. They are suitable for a high energy diet and provide protein, carbohydrates and fat, without being too bulky for those with small appetites.

INGREDIENTS	SERVES 4	SERVES 10
large baking potatoes, scrubbed	2	5
Tabasco sauce	few drops	½ tsp
egg yolks	5	13
crabmeat	625g/1½lb	1.25kg/3lb
breadcrumbs	150g/5oz	375g/12oz
red and green pepper, finely chopped	200g/7oz	425g/14oz
baby corn, finely chopped	25g/1oz	65g/2/12oz
salt and freshly ground black pepper		
olive oil, for deep frying		

METHOD

1 Preheat the oven to 200°C/gas mark 6 and bake the potatoes for 40–50 minutes until soft. Skin and mash and leave to cool completely.

2 Blend the Tabasco and egg yolks, combine with the crab, one third of the breadcrumbs, the peppers, baby corn and seasoning.

3 Mix lightly and form into rissoles, 2.5-cm/1-in thick and 8cm/3in long.

4 Place the remaining breadcrumbs in a shallow dish and roll the rissoles in the crumbs to coat.

5 Heat the olive oil in a wide frying pan over a low heat. Deep fry the rissoles until golden, drain, and serve.

NUTRITIONAL INFORMATION

Typical Values Per Portion
Energy 1916 K J / 456 Kcal
Protein 36.7g
Carbohydrate 40.3g
(of which sugars) (4.1) g
Fat 16.4g
(of which saturates) (3.1) g
Sodium 1,0g
Fibre 4.2g
Folate 53.28µg

Mango salsa

This delicious accompaniment supplies vitamins and minerals and can complement many meals.

INGREDIENTS (SERVES 10–15 AS AN ACCOMPANIMENT)

1 ripe mango, peeled and diced
3 ripe tomatoes, peeled, deseeded and chopped
1 red onion, finely chopped
1 tsp finely chopped fresh coriander
1 tsp toasted pine nuts
25g/1oz cucumber, finely diced
1 tbsp lemon or lime juice
1 tbsp olive oil
1 garlic clove, finely chopped
salt and freshly ground black pepper

METHOD

Combine all the ingredients well in a bowl and add the seasoning. Serve as an accompaniment to a variety of dishes.

Oven Baked Macaroni with Prunes & Nutmeg

Macaroni cheese has plenty of protein, which helps growth and repair. Our bodies do most of this work during the night so a supper dish of macaroni cheese is particularly good. In addition, the prunes help to keep our digestive system working well and add vitamin C to the dish.

INGREDIENTS	SERVES 4	SERVES 10
FOR THE CHEESE SAUCE:		
butter	50g/2oz	150g/5oz
flour	50g/2oz	150g/5oz
mustard powder	pinch	
milk	600ml/1 pint	1.5 litres/2½ pints
onion studded with cloves	1	2
bouquet garni	1	2
Gruyère cheese, grated	50g/2oz	150g/5oz
double cream	1 tbsp	3 tbsp
cayenne pepper	pinch	
canned prunes, pitted and chopped	100g/3½oz	300g/10oz
grated Parmesan cheese	25g/1oz	75g/3oz
salt and freshly ground black pepper		
macaroni	150g/5oz	400g/13oz
butter	15g/½oz	25g/1oz
pinch grated nutmeg		

Chef's tip: This cheese sauce can be used in a wide range of dishes. Remember to cook the sauce sufficiently to achieve a good taste. If the flour is not cooked enough before the milk is added, the sauce will taste starchy.

METHOD

1. Preheat the oven to 190°C/gas mark 5.
2. To prepare the cheese sauce, melt the butter in a saucepan, add the flour and mustard powder, cook over a medium heat, stirring constantly for 1 minute.
3. Add the milk gradually, mix well to ensure there are no lumps.
4. Add the onion and bouquet garni.
5. Simmer for 20 minutes.
6. Remove the onion and bouquet garni.
7. Add the Gruyère and mix well.
8. Add the cream, cayenne, and prunes and mix well, then add the seasoning.
9. Boil the macaroni in plenty of boiling salted water. Drain and toss in the butter.
10. Stir the cheese sauce into the pasta. Mix in the nutmeg and season.
11. Pour into an ovenproof serving dish.
12. Sprinkle with the grated Parmesan and cook for 15 minutes or until golden brown.
13. Serve with green salad or crusty bread.

Goat's Cheese & Red Pepper Tart

Chef's tip: Serve with a refreshing salad of baby plum tomatoes. Baking blind refers to partly cooking a pastry case before filling it. To prevent it rising, fill it with greaseproof paper filled with baking beans.

Goat's cheese was very popular in the 1940s and 50s, particularly with people living in the countryside. It is popular again now and there are many delicious recipes that incorporate it. This tasty vegetarian dish offers a range of textures, tastes, and colours in one lovely flan. It also supplies vitamins and minerals and makes good finger food if cut into handy slices.

INGREDIENTS	SERVES 4	SERVES 10
shortcrust pastry	200g/7oz	500g/1lb
red pepper	1	2
olive oil	3 tbsp	6 tbsp
onions, finely chopped	100g/3½oz	250g/8oz
clove garlic	1	2
fresh basil leaves	10	25
goat's cheese, sliced	50g/2oz	125g/4oz
salt and freshly ground black pepper		

METHOD

1. Preheat the oven to 180°C/gas mark 4.
2. Roll out the shortcrust pastry and use it to line 4 x 12-cm/4½-in individual tins.
3. Bake the pastry blind (see Chef's tip) for 20 minutes.
4. Preheat the grill to high. Skin the red pepper by brushing with 1 tbsp oil and grilling until blistered.
5. Heat 1 tbsp oil in a frying pan and sweat the onions and garlic golden brown.
6. Sprinkle the onions over the pastry.
7. Halve the peppers, remove the seeds, and cut into thin strips.
8. Place the pepper strips on top of the onions.
9. Arrange the basil and goat's cheese on the vegetables. Brush with the remaining olive oil and season.
10. Bake for 15 minutes until the cheese has melted and lightly coloured.

NUTRITIONAL INFORMATION

Typical Values Per Portion
Energy 1334 K J /320 Kcal
Protein 5.96g
Carbohydrate 26.3g
(of which sugars) (4,8) g
Fat 21.2g
(of which saturates) (6.4)g
Sodium 0,8g
Fibre 1.3g
Folate 12.00µg

Sweets & puddings

Sweet dishes are fun to prepare, so enjoy cooking delicious tempting sweets. Make your sweets with care and love for others to appreciate.

We have selected a delightful range of lovely puds that will really make the mouth water. There are creamy mousses, juicy ripe seasonal fruits, and traditional favourites with a new twist, all beautifully decorated.

Even when appetites are poor, most of us can be tempted to eat a little sweet delight. A fruit fool with cream, yoghurt, and fresh fruit is a light, easy to digest, and nourishing finish to a meal. A simple pudding can look wonderful and be very easy to prepare.

Use fresh and nutritious ingredients. It is a joy to see people derive such pleasure and good nutrition from these dishes.

Many people still love the old favourite puddings, such as bread and butter pudding, apple pie and custard, rice pudding, and sponge pudding. Many feel that they have not finished a meal unless they have enjoyed a great pudding. Entice appetites by ringing the changes with updated recipes. We have included a delightful Italian bread and butter pudding, which includes apples and wine. Serve fresh or stewed fruit with milk puddings or sponges to add vitamin C.

Diabetics can also eat sweets and puddings so don't assume that they can't have any sugar. You need to discuss their requirements with a dietician to ensure that you use the correct ingredients for the type of diabetes. You may have to substitute some sugar for an alternative, but you might be surprised at developments in diabetic diets developed on evidence-based research.

Although sugar and fat provide calories for energy and little else, the addition of eggs, fruit, and nuts can supplement the diet with protein, fibre, and many other nutrients.

Creamy Rice Pudding

Sometimes, poor appetites can be tempted with creamy milk puddings. Rice is a unique food; it offers protein, carbohydrate, vitamins, and some minerals. Supplemented with protein in the milk and carbohydrate for energy in the sugar, we have an all-round winner!

INGREDIENTS	SERVES 4	SERVES 10
butter	7g/¼oz	20g/¾oz
caster sugar	65g/2½oz	150g/5oz
pudding rice	65g/2½oz	150g/5oz
full fat milk	600ml/1 pint	1.25 litres/2¼ pints
vanilla essence	½ tsp	1 tsp
freshly grated nutmeg	pinch	½ tsp

METHOD

1 Preheat the oven to 150°C/gas mark 2.
2 Grease a 1.2-litre/2-pint pie dish with the butter. Place the sugar and rice in the dish.
3 Add the milk and vanilla essence and sprinkle the nutmeg on top.
4 Bake for 1½–2 hours.
5 Serve with Greek yoghurt and raspberry jam.

NUTRITIONAL INFORMATION

Typical Values Per Portion
Energy 682 K J /162 Kcal
Protein 4.5g
Carbohydrate 25.8g
(of which sugars) (17.0) g
Fat 4.5 g
(of which saturates) (2.8)g
Sodium trace
Fibre nil g
Folate 00µg

Rhubarb Crumble

Chef's tip: For extra fibre stir some porridge or jumbo oats into the crumble topping.

This is the ultimate crumble and most people's favourite, including the residents at Westgate House, who love this classic recipe.

INGREDIENTS	SERVES 4	SERVES 10
trimmed rhubarb, sliced	450g/15oz	1kg/2lb
golden syrup	2 tbsp	5 tbsp
pieces stem ginger, drained, finely chopped	2	5

FOR THE TOPPING:

	SERVES 4	SERVES 10
plain flour	100g/3½oz	250g/8oz
caster sugar	3 tbsp	8 tbsp
butter, diced	40g/1½oz	100g/3½oz

METHOD

1 Preheat the oven to 180°C/gas mark 4.
2 Put the rhubarb, syrup, and ginger into an ovenproof dish. Cover loosely with foil and bake for 10 minutes.
3 Put the flour, sugar, and butter into a mixing bowl, then rub in the butter with your fingertips or an electric mixer to form fine crumbs.
4 Remove the foil from the rhubarb, sprinkle the crumble over the top, and bake for 20–25 minutes until golden brown. Serve warm with vanilla ice cream or custard.

NUTRITIONAL INFORMATION

Typical Values Per Portion
Energy 634 K J / 151 Kcal
Protein 0.9g
Carbohydrate 21.0g
(of which sugars) (21.0) g
Fat 7.0g
(of which saturates) (3.0) g
Sodium 0.3g
Fibre 2.3g
Folate 19.98µg

Raspberry Fool

Chef's tip: Almost any fresh, raw or cooked fruit can be used for this simple but exciting dish.

This is an easy-to-eat dessert that provides vitamins from the raspberies and fat from the cream used, so is appropriate for a high energy diet.

INGREDIENTS	SERVES 4	SERVES 10
fresh raspberries	300g/10oz	700g
honey	2 tbsp	5 tbsp
lime, juice only	1	2
double cream	100ml/3½fl oz	250ml/8fl oz
thick Greek yoghurt	100ml/3½fl oz	250ml/8fl oz

FOR DECORATION:

double cream whipped with	50ml/2fl oz	125ml/4fl oz
vanilla essence and	3–4 drops	6–8
caster sugar	1 tbsp	2 tbsp
fresh raspberries		
sprigs of fresh mint		

METHOD

1 Purée the raspberries with honey, and pass through a sieve, if required, to remove pips.
2 Add the lime juice and adjust to taste.
3 Whisk the cream lightly and stir in the Greek yoghurt.
4 Mix half of the raspberry purée with half of the cream mixture.
5 In a tall sundae glass, starting with the raspberry mixture, layer the fruit, cream and the combined mixture, and finally another layer of fruit.
6 Cool in the fridge for two hours before serving.
7 To decorate, pipe on a rosette of vanilla cream and top with a raspberry and a sprig of mint to serve.

NUTRITIONAL INFORMATION

Typical Values Per Portion
Energy 1296 K J / 313 Kcal
Protein 3.9g
Carbohydrate 11.2g
(of which sugars) (11.2) g
Fat 28.1g
(of which saturates) (17.2) g
Sodium trace
Fibre 4.6g
Folate 29.34µg

Jam Roly-poly

Many older people prefer sweet foods to savoury, so we have included some old favourites that can be altered to suit most palates and diets. The roly-poly can be filled with fresh fruit instead of jam if preferred.

INGREDIENTS	SERVES 4	SERVES 10
self raising flour	200g/7oz	500g/1lb
vegetable suet	100g/3½oz	250g/8oz
pinch salt		
small lemon, finely grated zest and juice	1	2
medium egg, beaten	1	2
milk or water	2-4 tbsp	90-175ml/3-6fl oz
strawberry or raspberry jam	200g/7oz	500g/1lb
butter, for greasing	15g/½oz	25g/1oz
custard, cream or ice cream, to serve		

METHOD

1 Stir the flour, suet, salt, and lemon zest together, then work to a firm dough with the lemon juice, egg, and milk or water.

2 Roll out to a rectangle about 25 x 20cm/10 x 8in and spread jam to within 2.5cm/1in of the edges. Roll up, starting from a short end, and seal the edges well with a little water. For 10 portions, you can make one large roly-poly or two small ones.

3 Set the roll on a sheet of well-buttered foil and wrap, making sure the ends are well sealed.

4 Place the roly-poly into a steamer pan, electric steamer or combi oven. If you don't have a steamer you can cook this in the microwave for 12 minutes on high. Alternatively, fill a saucepan with water and place an upturned bowl inside. Place the roly-poly on top of the bowl to keep it out of the water, cover with a lid, and simmer for 1½–2 hrs. Check when cooked by putting a skewer into the pudding to see if it comes out clean.

5 Serve in slices with custard, cream or ice cream.

Chef's tip:
This is a very easy dish to make, but for best results make sure that you steam the roly-poly for the full 2 hours. There are many domestic electric steamers on the market that can be used for a wide range of foods. Steaming is a very healthy method of cooking as many of the nutrients are retained and the food remains moist.

NUTRITIONAL INFORMATION

Typical Values Per Portion
Energy 2163 K J / 516 Kcal
Protein 7.4g
Carbohydrate 68.6 g
(of which sugars) (28.3) g
Fat 23.6g
(of which saturates) (12.0) g
Sodium 0.2g
Fibre 1.1g
Folate 11µg

Treacle Sponge

Chef's tip: Adding treacle or maple syrup, instead of golden syrup, can ring the changes to this old favourite. It is also delicious served with a toffee sauce.

We were sent so many great pudding recipes, but this lovely, hearty, comforting one was our favourite. It is easy to make and offers plenty of carbohydrate and fat for high energy diets, especially when served with custard, cream or ice cream.

INGREDIENTS	SERVES 4	SERVES 10
golden syrup	2 tbsp	5 tbsp
fine white breadcrumbs	2 tsp	5 tsp
butter	100g/3½oz	500g/1lb
caster sugar	100g/3½oz	500g/1lb
lemon, grated zest only	1	3
eggs, beaten	2	5
self-raising flour	100g/3½oz	500g/1lb
salt	pinch	2 tsp
ground ginger	1 tsp	3 tsp
milk	75ml/3fl oz	250ml/8fl oz
butter, for greasing		

METHOD

1 Grease 1.2-litre/2-pint pudding basin with a knob of butter.
2 Mix together the syrup and breadcrumbs in the basin.
3 In a mixing bowl, cream the butter and, when very soft, add the sugar. Beat until light and fluffy. Add the lemon zest.
4 Gradually add the eggs, beating with each addition.
5 Sift and fold in the flour with the salt and ginger.
6 Add enough milk to make the mixture just loose enough to drop from a spoon.
7 Turn into the pudding basin, cover with two layers of greaseproof paper, tied under the lip of the basin firmly with string. If the pudding basin does not have a lip, tie the string halfway down the basin. Steam for 1½ hours. Alternatively, cook in the microwave for 12–15 minutes on high.
8 Turn out and serve with custard.

NUTRITIONAL INFORMATION

Typical Values Per Portion
Energy 1764 K J / 421 Kcal
Protein 4.0g
Carbohydrate 52.5g
(of which sugars) (32.1) g
Fat 21.7g
(of which saturates) (13.6) g
Sodium 0.5g
Fibre 0.3g
Folate 3.48µg

Italian Bread & Butter Pudding

*Chef's tip:
Add the third
apple to the
top bread layer
to enhance the
appearance.
Use sliced
pannetone
(Italian
Christmas
bread) instead
of white bread.*

Another great classic dish that is easy to make and can be enjoyed by people of all ages.

INGREDIENTS	SERVES 4–6	SERVES 10
butter	15g/½oz	40g/1½oz
small eating apples, peeled, cored and sliced into rings	3	7
caster sugar, plus a little extra to decorate	75g/3oz	200g/7oz
white wine	2 tbsp	5 tbsp
white bread, sliced, crusts removed if liked (slightly stale French baguette is ideal)	100g/3½oz	250g/8oz
single cream	300ml/½pt	900ml/1½ pints
eggs, beaten	2	5
small orange, grated zest only	1	2

METHOD

1 Lightly grease a 1.2-litre/2-pint deep ovenproof dish with butter. Arrange two thirds of the apple rings in the base of the dish. Sprinkle half the sugar over the apples, then add the wine.

2 Arrange the bread slices slightly overlapping on top of the apple, then tuck the remaining apple rings between the slices of bread. Push the bread down with your hands to flatten slightly.

3 Mix the cream with the eggs, the remaining sugar, and the orange zest, and pour the mixture over the bread. Leave to soak for 30 minutes.

4 Preheat the oven to 180°C/gas mark 4 for about 25 minutes until golden and set. Serve warm, sprinkled with a little extra sugar, if liked.

NUTRITIONAL INFORMATION

Typical Values Per Portion
Energy 1039 K J / 249 Kcal
Protein 5.5g
Carbohydrate 24.6g
(of which sugars) (16.8) g
Fat 13.8g
(of which saturates) (8.0) g
Sodium 0.2g
Fibre 1.1g
Folate 13.51µg

Yorkshire Cheesecake

Chef's tip: Preheat a baking sheet and then put the flan dish on top when baking to ensure that the base of the pastry is crisp.

This satisfying recipe is from Gladys West, who used to bake every Friday with her mum and later for her own family.

INGREDIENTS (SERVES 4–6)

100g/3½oz plain flour
pinch salt
25g/1oz butter
25g/1oz lard or white vegetable fat
4 tsp cold water

FOR THE FILLING:

250g/8oz curd cheese
75g/3oz caster sugar
1 tbsp golden syrup
1 lemon, grated zest only
2 eggs, beaten
50g/2oz currants
sieved icing sugar, to decorate

METHOD

1 Preheat the oven to 190°C/gas mark 5.
2 Put the flour into a bowl with the salt, add the fats and rub in with your fingertips, or an electric mixer, until fine crumbs form.
3 Mix in the water and lightly knead the pastry, then cover and chill for 20 minutes.
4 Roll out the pastry thinly on a lightly floured surface, then use to line a 18-cm/7-in diameter flan dish, trimming any excess pastry. Chill for a further 15 minutes.
5 Put the curd cheese, sugar, syrup, and lemon rind in a bowl and mix together. Gradually stir in the eggs then mix in the currants.
6 Pour the mixture into the pastry case, level the surface, and bake for 25–30 minutes until well risen and deep golden. Check halfway through cooking, and loosely cover with foil if the filling seems to be browning too quickly.
7 Dust with icing sugar and serve warm or cold.

NUTRITIONAL INFORMATION

Typical Values Per Portion
Energy 1459 K J / 347 Kcal
Protein 5.0g
Carbohydrate 54.0 g
(of which sugars) (35.8) g
Fat 12.4g
(of which saturates) (5.5) g
Sodium 0.1g
Fibre 0.5g
Folate 10.17µg

Apple Dumpling Pudding

Chef's tip:

This is great

served with fresh

custard or toffee

sauce. If you

would rather

have a cold

accompaniment,

try Greek yoghurt

or ice cream.

When she was a young girl, Barbara Clark made a pudding for the end of every main meal. This was her father's particular favourite.

INGREDIENTS	SERVES 4	SERVES 10
shortcut pastry	200g/7oz	500g/1lb
cooking apples, peeled and cored	4	10
lemon juice		
sugar	50g/2oz	125g/4oz
butter	50g/2oz	125g/4oz
milk, for brushing		
butter, for greasing		

METHOD

1 Lightly knead the pastry on a floured surface then roll out to a 30-cm/12-in circle. Cut out a quarter segment and reserve for the lid. Lift the remaining pastry onto a pudding basin and ease over the base and sides overlapping cut edges slightly and pressing together to seal.

2 Toss the apples in the lemon juice, then add to the lined basin with the sugar and butter.

3 Pat the reserved pastry into a circle the same size as the top of the pudding basin. Brush the top edges of the lined basin with a little milk, then press the pastry lid in place, trimming off any surplus pastry.

4 Cover with buttered and pleated greaseproof paper and foil, then tie in place with string, adding a string handle. Steam for 2 hours until well risen.

5 Serve with custard, yogurt or ice cream if you like.

NUTRITIONAL INFORMATION

Typical Values Per Portion
Energy 1222 K J / 292 Kcal
Protein 3.3g
Carbohydrate 37.5g
(of which sugars) (17.0) g
Fat 14.3g
(of which saturates) (4.4g
Sodium 203mg
Fibre 1.1g
Folate 4µg

Cakes & Biscuits

Enjoy baking different cakes and biscuits by adding extra ingredients for flavour and to supplement nutrition.

Serving crispy biscuits with morning coffee and delightful cakes with afternoon tea offer us further opportunities to supplement the diet and can make having coffee and tea very sociable. Laying pretty trays, or serving coffee and tea in the dining room, can make a real occasion of it.

Making cakes and biscuits can be very easy. We have included recipes in which everything goes into one bowl and is mixed together before cooking. There are also some more sophisticated bakes for those wishing to stretch their skills.

Impossible Pie

This recipe really does look and sound impossible, but it works so well every time – and is such fun to make – that we've left in the quantities used by residents.

MAKES A 25-CM/10-IN PIE
SERVES 6-8

4 eggs
½ cup/50g/2oz margarine
1 cup/200g/7oz white sugar
½ cup/50g/2oz self-raising flour
½ teaspoon salt
½ tsp baking powder
2 cups/475ml/16fl oz milk
1 cup/75g/3oz desiccated coconut
1 tsp vanilla extract
butter, for greasing

METHOD

1 Preheat the oven to 180°C/gas mark 4. Butter a 25-cm/10-in pie dish.
2 Place all the ingredients in a blender and process until thoroughly mixed.
3 Pour into the buttered pie dish. Bake for 1 hour.
4 When it's done, the crust will be on the bottom, custard in the middle, and coconut on top.

Chef's tip: I found it hard to believe that this recipe worked so well – and every time!

NUTRITIONAL INFORMATION

Typical Values Per Portion
Energy 1421 K J / 342 Kcal
Protein 5.3g
Carbohydrate 25.2g
(of which sugars) (25.1) g
Fat 24.4g
(of which saturates) (12.4g)
Sodium 0.2g
Fibre Nil
Folate 10.15 µg

Coffee & Walnut Sponge

Chef's tip: You could use half caster and half light muscovado sugar in the cake for additional flavour.

Joan Sudweeks, a resident at Winchester House has contributed this yummy sponge cake, a favourite for everyone on baking day.

MAKES AN 18-CM/7-IN CAKE

2 tsp instant coffee
1 tsp boiling water
65g/2½ oz walnut halves
175g/6oz butter or soft margarine
175g/6oz caster sugar
3 medium eggs
175g/6oz self raising flour
1 tsp baking powder

FOR THE FILLING:

1 tsp instant coffee
½ tsp boiling water
50g/2oz butter, at room temperature
100g/3½oz icing sugar, sifted, plus a little extra for decoration

METHOD

1 Preheat the oven to 180°C/gas mark 4.
2 Lightly oil, then line the bases of two 18-cm/7-in sandwich tins with greaseproof paper.
3 Put the coffee into a cup and dissolve in the boiling water. Reserve eight walnut halves for decoration and roughly chop the remainder.
4 Put the dissolved coffee and all the remaining cake ingredients into a bowl and beat together until smooth. Stir in the chopped walnuts.
5 Divide the cake mixture between the tins, level the surface and bake for 20 minutes until well risen and the tops spring back when lightly pressed with a fingertip.
6 Stand for 2–3 minutes then loosen the edges of the cakes and turn out on to a wire rack. Leave to cool.
7 To make the filling, dissolve the coffee in the boiling water. Beat the butter in a bowl until softened then gradually beat in the icing sugar until smooth. Stir in the coffee.
8 Peel the lining paper off the cakes, put one cake on to a serving plate, spread with the filling, add the second cake, and stick the reserved walnut halves on to the top with any filling still left in the bowl. Finish with a light dusting of sifted icing sugar.

NUTRITIONAL INFORMATION

Typical Values Per Portion
Energy 2089 K J / 501 Kcal
Protein 6.1g
Carbohydrate 49.5g
(of which sugars) (25.1) g
Fat 24.4g
(of which saturates) (15.7) g
Sodium 0.3g
Fibre Nil
Folate 4.70µg

Tea Time Treats

Chef's tip:

This is a very

simple but good

recipe, which

can be changed

by adding

different fruit,

covering with

chocolate, or

cutting into

different shapes.

These biscuits are easy to make and leave you wanting more. It's very hard to stick to one! Enjoy them with a cup of tea for a real tea time treat.

MAKES ABOUT 20 TREATS

125g/4oz butter
150g/5oz caster sugar
2 egg yolks
250g/8oz plain flour
1 orange, grated zest only
50g/2oz chopped dried fruit
1 level teaspoon of ground cinnamon

METHOD

1 Preheat the oven to 180°C/gas mark 4. Grease and flour a baking sheet.
2 Cream the butter and sugar together until pale.
3 Add the egg yolks and beat well.
4 Stir in the flour, orange zest, chopped fruit, and cinnamon until you have a firm dough.
5 Turn on to a lightly floured surface and knead lightly. Roll out to a thickness of 5mm/¼in.
6 Cut into about 20 5-cm/2-in rounds with a fluted cutter.
7 Place on the prepared baking sheet.
8 Cook for about 15 minutes until firm and very light brown.

NUTRITIONAL INFORMATION

Typical Values Per Portion
Energy 592 K J /141 Kcal
Protein 2.2g
Carbohydrate 17.8g
(of which sugars) (9.3) g
Fat 6.8g
(of which saturates) (3.7) g
Sodium trace
Fibre 0.1g
Folate 24µg

Banana & Walnut Bread

Eiddwen Thomas, a resident at Hafan Y Coed care home in South Wales, asked us to include his favourite afternoon treat.

MAKES A 500G/1LB LOAF

75g/3oz butter or margarine
100g/3½oz sugar
2 eggs
175g/6oz plain flour
1 teaspoon baking powder
½ tsp bicarbonate of soda
½ tsp salt
2-3 medium bananas, mashed
50g/2oz walnuts, chopped

METHOD

1 Preheat the oven to 170°C, gas mark 3. Grease a 500g/1lb loaf tin.
2 Cream the butter and sugar together in a large bowl.
3 Add the eggs and beat well.
4 Add the flour, baking powder, bicarbonate of soda, salt, and bananas and mix together.
5 Add the chopped walnuts and mix well.
6 Pour the mixture into the prepared loaf tin and cook for 50–60 minutes until a skewer inserted comes out clean and the loaf comes away from the sides of the tin.

Chef's tip: Add a good pinch of cinnamon for an interesting flavour.

NUTRITIONAL INFORMATION

Typical Values Per Portion
Energy 742 K J / 177 Kcal
Protein 3.7g
Carbohydrate 22.5g
(of which sugars) (12.7) g
Fat 8.0g
(of which saturates) (3.7)g
Sodium 0.2g
Fibre 1.0g
Folate 12.6µg

Barnbraek (Cold Tea Loaf)

Bill and Daphne Gibbons made Barnbraek tea loaf for special occasions as it was cheap and delicious.

MAKES A 500G/1LB LOAF

250g/8oz mixed dried fruit
175ml/6fl oz strained cold tea
250g/8oz self-raising flour, sieved
100g/3½oz light muscovado sugar
300g/10oz ground almonds
1 egg, beaten
2 tbsp milk

METHOD

1 Soak the dried fruit overnight in cold tea.
2 Grease and line a 500g/1lb loaf tin.
3 Preheat the oven to 180°C/gas mark 4.
4 Mix the flour, sugar, and ground almonds together in a bowl. Add fruit, tea, and egg and enough milk to make a dropping consistency.
5 Spoon into the tin, level the top and bake for about 1 hour, or until a skewer comes out clean when pushed into the centre of the loaf. If the top starts to brown too much, cover with foil.
6 Serve fresh for afternoon tea.

NUTRITIONAL INFORMATION

Typical Values Per Portion
Energy 1145 K J / 273 Kcal
Protein 8.1g
Carbohydrate 31.9g
(of which sugars) (19.6) g
Fat 12.6g
(of which saturates) (1.1) g
Sodium 0.1g
Fibre 1.0g
Folate 12.24µg

Chocolate Cake

Chef's tip:

To make chocolate squiggles melt 100g/3¹/₂oz cooking chocolate in the microwave for 2–3 minutes on defrost until runny. Drip the melted chocolate from a spoon onto silicone or greaseproof paper, making uneven squiggles, or drip straight onto the plate, if easier. Leave to set, peel off, and use to decorate the cake. This looks really professional and is so easy to do.

NUTRITIONAL INFORMATION

Typical Values Per Portion
Energy 1559 K J / 382 Kcal
Protein 3.9g
Carbohydrate 47.4g
(of which sugars) (37.4) g
Fat 19.5g
(of which saturates) (12.2) g
Sodium 0.2g
Fibre Nil
Folate 5µg

Everyone loves a chocolate cake and no recipe book would be complete without one. This simple recipe is great fun to decorate, as the squiggles can be as artistic as you like!

MAKES A 20-CM/8-IN CAKE
FOR THE CAKE:
75g/3oz flour
73g/3oz sugar
3 eggs
25g/1oz cocoa
1 tsp baking powder
150ml/½ pint milk

FOR THE FILLING:
100g/4oz butter
100g/4oz icing sugar, plus extra to dust
50g/2oz melted chocolate

METHOD
1 Preheat the oven to 180°C/gas mark 4. Grease and line two 20-cm/8-in round sandwich tins.
2 Combine all the cake ingredients together in a mixing bowl and beat well.
3 Pour into the prepared tins.
4 Bake for 15–20 minutes.
5 For the filling, cream the butter and sugar together. Stir in the melted chocolate and mix thoroughly.
6 Sandwich the cakes together with the butter cream. Dust the top lightly with icing sugar or decorate with chocolate squiggles (see Chef's tip).

Tea Scones

Chef's tip:

To keep scones

light just use

your fingertips

and combine the

ingredients gently.

Irene Coleman gave us this recipe. She used to cook for her family when her daughters were young (one is now 60 and the other 70 years old). She says that the secret of good scones is cool hands.

MAKES 8–10 SCONES

250g/8oz self raising four
pinch salt
25g/1oz sugar
25g/1oz butter
100g/3½oz currants
1 tbsp milk
1 egg
butter, for greasing

METHOD

1 Preheat the oven to 200°C/gas mark 6. Lightly grease a baking tray.
2 Sieve the flour and salt. Stir in the sugar and rub in the butter until it looks like fine breadcrumbs. Stir in the currants.
3 Combine the mixture together with fingers incorporating the milk and egg.
4 Put the scone mix into the fridge to rest for 10 minutes. Roll out the mixture to a thickness of 2cm/¾in and cut into 6-cm/2½-in round scones.
5 Place onto the greased tray and bake on the top shelf for 10–15 minutes until lightly browned.
6 Serve with butter, fresh cream and home-made strawberry jam for afternoon tea.

**NUTRITIONAL
INFORMATION**
Typical Values Per Portion
Energy 676 K J / 160 Kcal
Protein 3.7g
Carbohydrate 28.8g
(of which sugars) (10.4) g
Fat 3.3g
(of which saturates) (1.7) g
Sugar 8.49g
Sodium 0.2g
Fibre 0.7g
Folate 3.44µg

Oaty Biscuits

Chef's tip: Add raisins, chopped dates, apricots and nuts for a different taste.

Molly Teal was born into a family who loved food. During the War, her mother had a bread shop in Hull and Molly can remember the big panniers of rising dough in the hearth. Molly became a school cook; she used to make 300 of these oaty biscuits at a time!

MAKES 36 BISCUITS

250g/8oz plain flour
1½ tsp bicarbonate of soda
250g/8oz butter
250g/8oz caster sugar
250g/8oz porridge oats
1 tbsp milk
1¼ tsp almond essence
100g/3½ oz golden syrup, warmed

METHOD

1 Preheat the oven to 180°C/gas mark 4. Grease a baking sheet.
2 Sieve the flour with bicarbonate of soda.
3 Rub the butter into the flour and add the sugar and oats and mix well.
4 Add milk, essence, syrup, and melted butter. Combine well.
5 Divide the mixture into 36 rounds then roll into roughly shaped balls and put on two or three greased baking sheets. Flatten slightly with a fork.
6 Bake for 10 minutes or until crisp.
7 Remove from the baking sheet and allow to cool.

NUTRITIONAL INFORMATION

Typical Values Per Portion
Energy 561 K J / 134 Kcal
Protein 1.1g
Carbohydrate 16.3g
(of which sugars) (10.1) g
Fat 7.1g
(of which saturates) (4.4) g
Sodium 0.2g
Fibre Nil
Folate 1.47µg

Strawberry Shortbread

This is a shortbread recipe with a real difference. Shortbread is always delicious but with cream and strawberries it's totally irresistible.

MAKES 10 SHORTBREAD:
100g/3½oz plain flour
50g/2oz semolina
100g/3½oz butter
50g/2oz caster sugar
25g/1 oz flaked almonds (optional)
a little caster or demerara sugar, for dusting

FOR THE FILLING:
125ml/4fl oz double or whipping cream
25g/1oz caster sugar
a few drops vanilla extract
250g/8oz fresh strawberries, sliced

METHOD
1 Preheat the oven to 170°C/gas mark 3.
2 Mix the flour with the semolina in a bowl. Add the butter and sugar and rub together with your fingertips, until the mixture is just beginning to bind together. Knead lightly until the mixture forms a smooth dough.
3 Roll the dough out to a thickness of 5mm/½in thick. Cut into 20 rounds with a 7.5cm/3in biscuit cutter, bake in the oven for 10–15 minutes or until a very pale golden brown.
4 Leave to cool for a few minutes then place on a cooling rack and sprinkle with sugar.
5 To make the filling: whip the cream with the vanilla extract and sugar.
6 Sandwich the shortbread rounds together with cream and strawberries.

NUTRITIONAL INFORMATION
Typical Values Per Portion
Energy 1046 K J / 252 Kcal
Protein 3.0g
Carbohydrate 19.2g
(of which sugars) (7.7) g
Fat 18.1g
(of which saturates) (10.4) g
Sodium 0.1g
Fibre 1.1g
Folate 4.11µg

Index

Ideas for Finger Foods

Sweet potato and feta rosti **page 38**
Chicken with sage, onion and cranberry (without sauce) **page 55**
Seafood parcels with crème fraiche and dill **page 56**
Citrus crusted salmon goujons **page 57**
Salmon fishcakes **page 60**
Parma ham wrapped salmon **page 62**
Cornish pasties **page 76-77**
Cumberland sausage (without mash) **page 78**
Toad in the hole (without gravy) **page 80**
Resident's pizza **page 82**
Leek & brie tart **page 87**
Crab & baby corn rissoles **page 90**
Goat's cheese & red pepper tart **page 94**
Jam roly poly (without custqrd) **page 101**
Yorkshire cheesecake **page 106**
All cakes and biscuits **pages 110-125**